"Taste has no price tag"

Ever since two notched logs were joined to create the first log cabin by our Pilgrim Fathers, the making of a happy home has been near and dear to the heart of the American.

Our country's first "professional" decorators were men who went from house to house with a satchel of brushes and stencils strapped to their backs. For board and room they stenciled walls and floors to simulate the pattern of scarce and costly damasks and carpets.

Thomas Jefferson, while best known as a statesman, had outstanding talent for both interior and exterior design, and his beauitful home Monticello is a rich source of decorating ideas. Although Monticello was not a typical American home, since it was the home of a man of great wealth, it is an example of one of the two classifications into which I feel interior design falls. These two classifications are "formal" and "informal."

Usually the formal tends to be synonymous with expensive furnishings and the informal with more economically priced merchandise. However, the reverse can often be found. For example, the straight simple lines of Shaker furniture in a small cottage can spell formality, while the luxurious home of a millionaire movie star can reflect informality and casual living.

There is no price tag on taste, so whether your budget is small or large, you still face the same effort in the creation of a beautiful, hospitable home. The decoration of a home is so personal a task that it must be tailored to the individual needs of its occupants.

I offer the following comments with the hope that among the pages that follow you will find ideas and information applicable to your needs.

Paul Krauss

PAUL KRAUSS, A.I.D.

PAUL KRAUSS has been described by the press as an untemperamental interior designer of rare imagination, initiative and talent. Before opening his own firm, he was for years decorating editor of *Living for Young Homemakers* magazine. He has designed offices for our country's top executives, homes for the socially prominent as well as celebrities of the theatrical and literary world. Unlike many of his colleagues, his interest is not confined to the upper-bracket dollar. He is frank to admit that his greatest professional satisfaction came from a budget one-room apartment. While in the army, his talents were evident throughout Burma and India in the form of theaters and productions ingeniously created from materials provided by the jungle. Hoosier born and bred, Mr. Krauss, with his wife and son, now lives a split life between a New York apartment and a small 18th century country house in Connecticut.

COPYRIGHT 1967
TELL CITY CHAIR COMPANY
TELL CITY, INDIANA

The Entrance Area

The entrance creates a first impression and should say, "Welcome!" It is the ideal place to vent your desire for the dramatic because people pass through it rather than live in it. Here is the place for the bold, colorful wallpaper or the black and white tile floor with a strong wall color. This is also the place where thoughtful appointments make a guest feel more welcome — like a console and mirror where a woman can make her final lipstick check. A small settle here is also most convenient. A guest closet is usually, by virtue of its name, a joke. Instead of an area containing hangers and shelf space reserved for a guest, the door opens and out tumbles everything, from roller skates to the recently delivered cleaning and laundry. No house has enough storage space and near the front door is an ideal location for it. As most foyers are more or less waste space, why not use all the walls for storage? One entrance hall I remember had shelves from ceiling to floor, utilizing all of the space that usually is wasted. These had frames of 1" x 3" lumber and window shades of laminated crewel print in green and white. One of the concealed sections contained clothes hangers for guests, another for the family. The floor was white vinyl marbleized with black to camouflage soil, accented with a large area rug of a brilliant blue and green geometric pattern.

The Living Room

The living room must double in brass. It is the room in which guests are entertained and for that reason alone the one in which the most effort and money are spent. In addition, it has to be comfortable and functional for all the family's needs. It should have well-scaled upholstered seating pieces for relaxation, and good lighting to provide the best possible reading conditions. Arrange a maximum number of large stationary seating pieces augmented with floater or auxiliary chairs that can join and expand the seating. If the room is large, the arrangement should divide into two or more groups. It is virtually impossible for more than six people to carry on a conversation without interrupting each other or naturally dividing into smaller groups. So why put barriers in the way of pleasant talk by insisting upon a single large group of seating pieces? You must also consider traffic patterns in arranging your room. Allow convenient passages so people on the move do not interrupt seated groups. A living room that is used only as a status symbol and not really enjoyed and lived in as the name implies, is a

tremendous waste of space in a house. If you are fortunate enough to have a family room or den as well, the living room can be furnished in a less practical vein than when it takes the entire burden of everyday living.

The Family Room

The family room should be an intimate area. Here is a good place for your most personal possessions. Very much at home are pictures of friends and family, either in easel frames dominating a large table or covering an entire wall. Certainly the family room should not be "second best," a place for discarded furniture. The television set is apt to be here, leaving the

living room free from distraction. The family room often serves as a dining or snacking area with its table used for many things including family games, hobbies, and homework. For this reason it should have a durable top — like Formica which now is so expertly grained that you can hardly tell it from real wood. Easy maintenance is desirable. A floor that can be vacuumed or mopped is a good idea. Coverings of sturdy tweeds or slipcovers that can be laundered make sense here. All games and hobbies should be easily available in this room, so provide plenty of cupboards.

The Dining Room

If you have a dining room, you are fortunate and should make the most of it. One of the most gracious and functional pieces is a large buffet/hutch. This, in addition to providing a place for silver and linen, can function as a serving table for buffet suppers at which guests can help themselves and then sit down to a well-appointed table. One clever hostess I know entertained a rather large group with a curry supper. The condiments were attractively arranged on the upper shelves of the hutch and a small drawer in the buffet base had been emptied and filled with hot rolls wrapped in a napkin. The dining table should be expandable so you can seat a few or many. I strongly believe that all should be seated on matching chairs, no matter how many are at the table. The wisest buyers I know purchase eight or ten matched side chairs and then use them all over the house — in bedrooms, halls, foyer, or at a desk. A pair of pull-up chairs from the living room can serve as host and hostess chairs to further enlarge the matched seating. These may easily be different in color, size and design. For every woman who likes to dine by candlelight, there is usually a masculine voice grumbling that he refuses to eat what he cannot see. The happy solution is a combination of candlelight and lamplight. Simply put a lamp on a serving table or sideboard to help the decorative but inadequate candles. Most attractive and functional are chandeliers with real candles and a small electric light in the base to reflect directly on the table top. When lighting the dining room, or any room for that matter, avoid a general glare. Rather, create enough light in the desired areas and leave less important parts of the room in shadow for contrast and interest. You don't have to place your table in the center of the room. You can place it off center and use the room also as a study, game room, library, or music room (with the addition of a small piano). A harvest table with its long, narrow leaves, can go in front of a window with one leaf lowered so that diners can enjoy the view while they eat. When guests are expected, the table can be moved to the center with both leaves raised. This table also serves beautifully as a table top desk used at right angles from the wall or window with one leaf raised. The main consideration is maximum use of your dining room. Most people really can't afford to set aside one room for mealtime use only.

The Bedroom

The bedroom should be the most individualistic of all rooms. Unlike other areas that must serve a variety of ages and interests, the bedroom can be designed to suit one person, and one only. Here daughter can indulge in the most feminine of whims and son can start at an early age to defend the theory that a man's home is his castle. No child's room should be simply a place to sleep because here he or she has the opportunity to express the desire for individuality. A good desk is an investment with years of use ahead. One simple shelf has been known to be the beginning of a library and a genuine love of reading. Bedrooms should contain as many appointments for comfort, convenience, and luxury as possible. If you and your husband enjoy reading, a pair of triangular pillows will make you comfortable. Slipcover them in the same print as your draperies. Large bedside tables and good lamps also contribute greatly. I remember seeing a desk at right angles to the wall and next to and parallel to the bed. This arrangement created an ideal combination bedroom and study. A comfortable chair or two are always welcome additions. Be sure to arrange furniture so that the dressing area is convenient to closets and chests.

Early American Furniture
IN A MODERN BACKGROUND

A beautiful antique painting comes to life against the stark simplicity of a modern museum setting. A cigar-store Indian comes into focus more clearly when it leaves the store front and is placed against a plain wall. So it is with Early American furniture. Used in a modern setting, every line and carving stands out in all its beauty. This is why the soft, familiar, classically traditional furniture is at home in a modern house. It looks equally well against a wall of glass or beside the traditional tall window with tie-back draperies. Using Early American furniture against a background of contemporary architecture might well be a solution for the couple with conflicting tastes for modern or traditional.

Ways to achieve the Early American Look

RANDOM PLANKING

Crate wood, which is the cheapest available lumber, makes a beautiful wall when used floor to ceiling and painted flat white to give the appearance of whitewash. It can be used as a single wall in a room or for all four. It is full of irregular knots and splits. These as well as the variation in the cracks between planks all add to the interest and texture of the surface. Weathered barn siding used in random widths is also much in demand these days as a wall covering. It is beautiful in old weather-faded colors such as pale gray-blue, barn red and sun-bleached silver gray. If you can't find the faded color you want, use old rough-sawn lumber, apply a very thin coat of flat paint, and rub with a rag to achieve an authentic effect. To produce the silvery effect of old boards, apply aluminum paint very thin, wipe it, and then apply burnt umber. Vertical planks on the wall will create an illusion of height.

WAINSCOTING

If you want to cut down the height of your walls, use horizontal lines to achieve the illusion of width. This can be done with a chair rail or wainscoting. Stock chair rail molding can be obtained from any lumber dealer and applied about 30 inches from the floor. The exact height

will depend on the proportion of your room. Experiment a bit before you nail it in place. Paint the woodwork and wainscoting, including the area below, a color to match or harmonize with the background of the wallpaper used above the wainscoting. Wallpaper murals also are very effective.

SELECTING PAINT COLORS

The easiest covering to apply, of course, is paint. This should be a flat finish. In picking a color, remember that it reflects against itself in a room if it is used on more than one wall and intensifies considerably. You can get a pretty good idea of how a certain color will look by making a viewing tube as follows: Paint the color on a piece of paper a couple of feet square. When dry, roll it into a tube. Look into the tube as you would a telescope. You will then see clearly how the color will look on all four walls, reflecting against itself. It is surprising how a very pale color will intensify and come way up in strength. When you are ready to choose a color, be sure you have available all other colors that you are going to use. Remember that the wall color so outweighs the other elements that it can afford to be much more subdued. If you look at some of the best wall colors without considering the other hues you plan to use in the room, they will look very dull and uninteresting, indeed. This is particularly true of the quieter colors. I call these the "nothing" colors because they are a big letdown from your stronger

colors. These include the very grayed greens and the soft, restful putty colors with a greenish cast that are neither beige nor gray but in between. These look hopeless by themselves. However, as a background for the woods and fabrics you will put before them, they are perfect. If your room is badly shaped or cut up by structural beams, a good way to minimize the deficiencies of the architecture is to paint ceilings, walls, and woodwork all the same color. Use very pale, muted, soft colors, white or off-white. A strong color would tend to be heavy.

FABRICS FOR WALLS

Fabrics are used as wall coverings with great success these days. It is certainly not a new idea. We see fine damasks in the early houses of our ancestors as well as in the châteaus of France. Fabric can be applied to the walls with a wallpaper paste just as you would apply paper. It can also be stapled or tacked at the top and bottom and finished with a gimp or braid. Fasten it either directly to the wall or to lath applied to the wall at the ceiling and floor. Sometimes the widths of fabric are sewn together first so that the whole wall is one piece. The windows and doors are cut out after the fabric is in place. Since fabric costs more than paper, you might restrict its use to the wall from chair rail to ceiling and use paint or wood below.

CROWN MOLDING

To create a Colonial feeling in an otherwise uninteresting room, use a crown molding around the top of the wall where it joins the ceiling. (For sketches of this and other types of moldings, see bottom of page 7.) It should be mitered at the corners or wherever it turns a corner. Dentil molding is particularly handsome. There are a variety of crown moldings in many widths available through your local lumber dealer. Here is a good rule of thumb on how to treat woodwork: When it is an asset to a room, paint it a strong contrasting color. When it is a detriment, paint it the same color as the walls so it will tend to blend out of sight.

FIREPLACES

Most fireplaces can be treated to give them an Early American look. These sketches show a couple of simple examples. Some mantels and special effects are available ready-made from lumber dealers. Others can be achieved with stock moldings cut with a miter box. If you tuck your fireplace dimensions away in your purse, you may find a beautiful old pine mantel when you are least expecting it. It is an example of how, by being alert, you can gradually create the kind of Early American home you want. Remember, most builders provide only the basic necessities. It is up to you to give them character with your addition of moldings, paint, wallpapers, and floor coverings.

VINYL FLOORS

There is hardly a limit to what you can do with vinyl flooring. You can get random plank patterns, black and white squares, plain or marbleized coverings, solid colors with a spatter dash pattern, brick and tile, whitewashed brick, pink brick or conventional red brick designs all laid in a basket weave pattern, ceramic tile designs in white, pale green

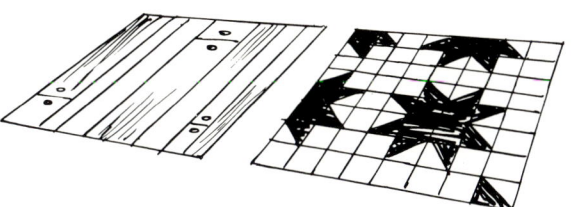

or the traditional terra cotta. The illustrated traditional quilt design which is very unusual and effective is made from standard 9" x 9" squares.

STENCILED FLOORS

Most Early American floors were made of wide planks, frequently chestnut and other woods that are hard to get today. However, the early traveling decorators who stenciled patterns on floors and walls created some beautiful designs. You can follow their example with a little determination and effort. If you don't want to tackle an entire floor, try decorating the

risers on your stairs. Early stencils were cut in paper and coated with wax. The most successful I have seen today are cut in transparent lucite or plastic. This simplifies positioning. Here are the few instructions you need: Use a flat color. Keep the stencils free from paint on the underside. Use paint sparingly on the brush. Mix enough paint to complete the work. Cut a separate stencil for each color. And don't worry about the color being exactly uniform. The easiest way to lay out a pattern on the floor is with a chalk line. This way, you can divide your floor into units, each representing the pattern to be stenciled. After you have completed stenciling, apply a coat of flat varnish and then wax it to protect your handiwork.

OTHER FLOORS

One of the most unusual floors I have ever seen was in a foyer. It was covered with a spectacular printed wallpaper and then given three coats of clear varnish and waxed. I don't know how long it lasted,

but its effectiveness more than outweighed the labor and minimum expense involved. It might show the wear and tear in a few years, but don't we all? Dark stained floors, and I mean *really* dark, are a fine foundation for a room. They must be sanded and finished in a very dark walnut brown-black stain. This surface should then have a waxy finish but not a high gloss. Such dark floors provide a beautiful background for hooked, woven or braided rugs. The extreme opposite is equally effective. One of the smartest and most expensive apartments I have seen had a white painted floor spattered in beige. A small, shaggy area rug of white fur was thrown in front of the couch. It provided softness and yet kept a unity and consistency to the floor surface. The walls were also white which sharply silhouetted the fine woods of the furniture and accentuated the fresh, vital colors of the furniture coverings.

HOOKED RUGS

Hooked rugs are great with Early American furniture, particularly when they are homemade. Just as a cake made from scratch is better than a mix, so are your own designs far superior to those made "by the numbers." Remember, the cruder the better. The highest prices at auctions are bid for the old hooked rugs that make Grandma Moses' work look like the product of a slide rule. A hearth rug on a plain bare floor can be the focal point as well as the conversation piece of a room. Braided rugs can be as alive and up to date in color as you are willing to make them. Don't think of a braided rug as the final resting place for your hus-

band's old overcoat or Sunday suit. If the pants are shiny, find some other excuse to get him to buy a new suit. Start with *colorful* woolen scraps in lemon-peel yellow, strong avocado, tangerine and white, or a scheme of mustard, scarlet, black and white. Make long enough braids in *each* color (not mixed) so they will stand out alone in the rug. You can sometimes add spice to a length of braid by combining colors that are in the same family but clash — like pinks and reds or oranges and pinks. This will really make your rug sing. Early American need not be dreary. It can be subdued, soft, restful, relaxing but *not dreary*. Most of the dark, faded colors we associate with Early American exist because they have either faded with time or were colored with chemicals that did not provide a strong hue. After all, have you ever tried dyeing something with a few crushed berries? Make vibrant rugs by using clear, bright colors. It's worth the effort.

NEEDLEPOINT RUGS

If you enjoy needlework, here's a chance to show your talents. Actress Shirley Booth kept her fingers busy between scenes of Hazel by turning out a masterpiece of gros point. As a finished rug, it rests in front of a beautiful Early American chest in her study and creates as many compliments as her academy-award-winning artistry. There is something enviable about a home possessing the craftsmanship of an enthusiastic artisan, be it a stenciled floor, a hooked rug, or a fine piece of needlepoint.

FACTORY-MADE RUGS

Don't get the idea that the only solution to the floor problem is through the work of your hands. Actually, many manufacturers produce beautiful area and room size rugs that complement and coordinate Early American furniture. They are available in both fresh and subdued

Window Treatments

TO ESTABLISH THE EARLY AMERICAN LOOK

One of the most important decorative contributions in a room is the window treatment. The styling of these can create period and character in a room. In addition to these sketches you can find many ideas in historical homes, museums, and

your local library. In many houses of today I find what are called privacy windows. These are narrow slits that are placed awkwardly high on the wall. Granted people can't see in, but neither can you see out. Anyway, my advice is to treat them as much like the wall as possible. If the wall is painted, make plain curtains of a matching color sheered on a rod and hung within the reveal of the window. Then if the builder has been generous enough to provide you with some normal windows elsewhere in the room, dramatize them with an eye-catching print using drapery and valance. The privacy window will be absorbed as just part of a plain wall and the attention and interest will center on the proper windows. I once saw a really old house in which partitions had been removed and a bay window added so that the symmetry of the room had long been forgotten. The large bay was draped in a beautiful documentary print and the various sized and oddly shaped windows were dressed with two tiers of sheered white

colors. Wall-to-wall carpeting is practical in terms of maintenance. Today's color range is limitless. If your home is small, I recommend that you use the same carpet color throughout. The color will provide a unity and minimize the cut-up effect of a small house. A good overall approach is to treat a small house as one big room arranged in areas rather than a lot of separate, different rooms. There is no law demanding a different color, different pattern, different style, after you cross each threshold. One way to tie things together is to use the same color on the wall in one room that you use on the furniture in another. Or you can repeat the carpet color on one wall of a room and on three walls of another. Your eye has a way of remembering, even if you are not conscious of it.

curtains made of sheeting. Since the walls were white, no one ever noticed that the windows were at different heights, of different sizes, and in odd places.

Other effective window treatments can be achieved with the use of inside shutters. These are available in stock sizes and can be practical or just ornamental with movable or stationary louvers. Shutters can be made of plywood and covered with fabric or wallpaper. I have also seen shutter frames constructed of 1" x 2" clear pine frames with panels of sheered fabric.

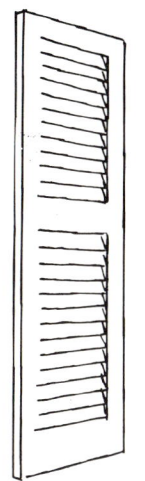  

If you have a window with a bad view, you might sheer a fabric on a rod at both top and bottom so that it is stretched tight within the reveal of the window. Window shades are available in wonderful colors today and come both translucent and room darkening. Laminated window shades are available in your own fabric. Venetian blinds existed long before the 18th century and, of course, are as practcal today as they ever were in terms of controlling light and air.

How to Estimate Yardage
FOR DRAPERIES AND CURTAINS

When estimating yardage for draperies, you need to establish two facts:
1. The width of the fabric.
2. The repeat of the design of the fabric.

Draperies should have 100% fullness, thus an opening six feet wide requires four widths of 36" fabric. For the length of each fabric strip allow a minimum one foot extra for heading turnover and bottom hem. This is simple in a plain fabric. However, if the repeat in the pattern is very large, I suggest you take your window measurements to the place where you buy your fabric and let them figure it out. It is much better to use a lot of an inexpensive fabric than to skimp with an expensive one. Some of the most effective draperies I have seen were hanging at very tall windows. They were made of heavy canvas drop cloths and were bordered in an expensive large heavy cotton fringe. Casement and glass curtains should be more than 100% full if the material is very open. If you don't want to open and close them frequently these can be sheered on a rod with a heading. This is much cheaper than having them pinch pleated. They can go to the sill or, if you want to create a feeling of French doors, they can go to the floor. When planning the length of short curtains, try to find a logical stopping place for them such as the window sill, or the bottom of the molding just beneath.

HOW TO ESTIMATE YARDAGE FOR SLIP COVERS

WING CHAIR	UPHOLSTERY: 50" Fabric ....6 Yds. SLIP COVER: 50" Fabric ....8 Yds. 36" Fabric ....10 Yds. SKIRT ....1½ Yds.	CLUB CHAIR LOOSE BACK	UPHOLSTERY: 50" Fabric ....7 Yds. SLIP COVER: 50" Fabric ....10 Yds. 36" Fabric ....13 Yds. SKIRT ....1 Yd.
ARM CHAIR	UPHOLSTERY: 50" Fabric ....3 Yds. Do not slip cover chair or couch with tight seat — cushion seat only.	TIGHT BACK SOFA	UPHOLSTERY: 50" Fabric ....10½ Yds. SLIP COVER: 50" Fabric ....12 Yds. 36" Fabric ....20 Yds. SKIRT ....2 Yds.
OPEN ARM CHAIR	UPHOLSTERY: 50" Fabric ....2¼ Yds. SLIP COVER: 50" Fabric ....2½ Yds. 36" Fabric ....3 Yds. SKIRT ....1½ Yds.	LOVE SEAT LOOSE BACK	50" Fabric ....8 Yds. SLIP COVER: 50" Fabric ....9½ Yds. 36" Fabric ....13 Yds. SKIRT ....1 Yd.

Stock Moldings TO HELP ACHIEVE THE EARLY AMERICAN LOOK

By adding a few stock moldings over a simple mantel to create panels, a crown molding at the ceiling and a chair rail around the room, you can create a very effective Early American feeling. Painting this woodwork one of the traditional Colonial colors, such as barn red, Pennsylvania Dutch gray-blue, mustard yellow or dirty bottle green will provide effective contrast to plaster white walls.

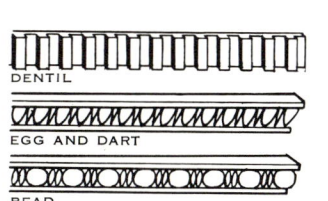

1865-1967
Over one hundred years of fine furniture craftsmanship

The average resident of Tell City, Indiana has sawdust in his veins — because he and his forefathers have been living and breathing furniture-making for a hundred years.

The first of the Tell City craftsmen journeyed down the Ohio by paddleboat in the 1860's after migrating from Switzerland and Germany. They settled in the little Indiana community named after the Swiss hero, William Tell, and immediately began practicing the trade they had learned in the old country.

Before long, these thrifty artisans pooled their meager resources and formed the beginnings of Tell City Chair Company. Called "Chair Makers Union," the firm began making splint bottom chairs which a company spokesman described as follows:

"Our chairs are different from those mostly in the market because we aim to make good splint bottom chairs."

This was the first written statement of company policy. Its spirit stands today and is your assurance of good value.

Tell City Chair Company still makes *good* furniture — not only chairs and rockers, but correlated dining room, bedroom and living room furniture as well . . . such as the Young Republic Group featured in this book.

Now one of the oldest and largest furniture manufacturers in the nation, the firm has expanded into nearly half a million square feet of space in four factories.

The original handful of skilled artisans has passed its tradition of fine craftsmanship on to third and fourth generation workers who are among the 1,000 present Tell City employees.

THE ORIGINAL FACTORY OF THE "CHAIR MAKERS UNION" AS SHOWN IN AN OLD 1875 LITHOGRAPH.

AN EARLY PICTURE, TAKEN IN THE 1880'S, OF EMPLOYEES OF THE "CHAIR MAKERS UNION."

First products

Pattern No. 1 was the double cane splint bottom chair. Through 1906, this chair was the principal product. In the early 1900's the company was producing 1,000 dozen per week and called itself "the largest manufacturers of double cane chairs in the world." Since then, Tell City has manufactured more than 30,000,000 chairs alone.

PATTERN NO. 1

The first Tell City Chair Company products were completely handmade. Over the years the company has completely modernized its production techniques to achieve efficiency, yet, by choice, retains many hand operations. Only in this way is it possible to preserve the handcrafted character that is a hallmark of fine Tell City furniture.

In a sense, the designers of Tell City's Young Republic Group have one foot in the 18th century and the other in the 20th. They draw their inspiration from authentic Early American patterns that were developed during the birth of our nation. They translate them into pieces that are scaled to 20th century living and built to the standards of 20th century comfort.

When you examine the Young Republic Group of Dining, Living and Bedroom furniture, each piece will speak for itself — the satin-smooth finish; the vibrant, clear grain; the friendly, openhearted design. But behind each piece you will also have the assurance of over 100 years of fine craftsmanship, Tell City's strong conviction that you are entitled to good value, and a tradition of designing that keeps Young Republic in perfect taste for all the years of your life.

Chair wagons like this rolled through local streets for more than half a century delivering chair frames to homes for hand seating and picking up the finished chairs.

Chairs were delivered to the wharf boat where they were loaded on paddle-wheel boats for shipment to furniture dealers.

The secret of Young Republic's everlasting appeal to lovers of Early American

WHEN YOU SELECT EARLY AMERICAN FURNITURE KEEP THESE <u>FIVE</u> IMPORTANT AREAS IN MIND

1. DESIGN

Young Republic is the kind of furniture you would design for yourself if you knew how or had the time. It is a natural furniture for our day because it reflects our character as a people just as surely as its prototypes some 200 years ago. This is why good Early American will never get out of date. It is our "folk" furniture just as surely as the leather and carved wood furniture is indigenous to Spain and bamboo pieces speak the language of the Far East.

Although it takes its inspiration from the early days of our nation, Young Republic is no slavish copy of early patterns. Let's face it — we expect to be more comfortable than our pioneer forefathers. And, believe it or not, we are not even the same shape! Generally, we are several inches taller, which is why king-size mattresses are selling. So Young Republic is scaled to the modern man and woman and all seating pieces are built for comfort. Likewise, Young Republic is scaled to today's homes, and today's way of life.

Summing it up, the "secret" of Young Republic's everlasting appeal to lovers of Early American is that it contains the soul of our American heritage, but with functional and constructional improvements to meet the needs of modern living.

2. SELECTION

Young Republic offers one of the largest, most complete lines of Early American furniture for dining rooms, kitchens, bedrooms, living rooms, family rooms, and dens. You will find exactly the combination of furnishings that reflects your individual taste. And most important, Young Republic is open stock! Buy what you can afford now and add matching or coordinating pieces later as your budget permits. You can be completely confident that all Young Republic pieces, with their great variety of styles and sizes, will maintain the same continuity of character. They will always complement your decor, whether you match or mix Young Republic patterns. As an added convenience to you, Tell City delivers orders quickly from its modern plants to your dealer.

3. WOOD

Our pioneer furniture makers used whatever wood was at hand, hard or soft. But much of the furniture that came out of early New England was particularly cherished because it was made from Hard Rock Maple. This continues to be the preferred wood for Early American furniture because it is close grained and sturdy as well as beautiful. And, since only solid wood can convey the authentic feeling of Early American design, all Young Republic furniture is the finest quality Solid Hard Rock Maple.

4. FINISH

The warm brown Andover finish that characterizes the Young Republic Group closely matches the mellow look of authentic Early American antiques. Instead of being built up by layers on top of the wood, Tell City's finish actually penetrates the wood itself and permits the grain to show through in all its natural beauty. Since the finish is such an integral part of the wood, it allows the natural hardness of Solid Hard Rock Maple to resist wear and abuse. A good finish starts with the sanding operation. For years, the cabinetmakers' rule of thumb has been, "Well sanded is half finished." Tell City takes particular pains in preparing each piece by sanding it many times before the penetrating tone is applied. This assures a finish that is satiny rather than glassy, with the wood color and pattern vibrantly alive and beautiful.

5. SATISFACTION

Since most construction features in furniture are hidden from view, your best guarantee of quality is the manufacturer's experience and reputation. Here at Tell City we take particular pains to build satisfaction into our products so that you will experience the day-to-day joy of using fine furniture as well as being proud of its beauty. We use the best Hard Rock Maple and other materials and carefully craft each piece. Drawers are dovetailed, have center guides, and are dustproofed. Many design features, such as pilasters, not only contribute beauty, but also strengthen the case. All buffets, dressers, chests and tables are solidly corner-blocked and braced. Each is engineered to allow for the natural expansion and contraction of solid woods. Chairs are built for sturdiness. Slats, for instance, are steam bent to retain the full strength of the long grain. Back posts go all the way through the seat and have wooden wedges pounded in to form an unusually tight bond (just like the handle of a hammer). There are many hand operations, including the weaving of fibre seats right on the chair frames. Careful designing includes engineering rocking chairs so they balance perfectly while at rest as well as when in use.

We offer you Young Republic with all the pride and confidence of our more than one hundred years of fine furniture craftsmanship. You will use it with pride and confidence and continue to enjoy it when your grandchildren are old enough to furnish their own homes with Young Republic. Each piece is tagged with our guarantee, clearly stated.

SOLID HARD ROCK MAPLE GROUP

Young Republic meets all your requirements!

GUARANTEE

This product of the Tell City Chair Company is guaranteed for one year from date of purchase to be free from defects in workmanship and material under normal household use and care. This guarantee does not apply to damage resulting from negligence, misuse or accidents, nor does it apply to wearing quality and colorfastness of fabrics.

Any defect should be reported to the dealer from whom your purchase was made; he will make all arrangements for you.

Products defective under the terms of this guarantee will be repaired or replaced at manufacturer's option, free of charge.

There's a difference in Maple!

ALL YOUNG REPUBLIC PIECES ARE MADE FROM

Solid Hard Rock Maple

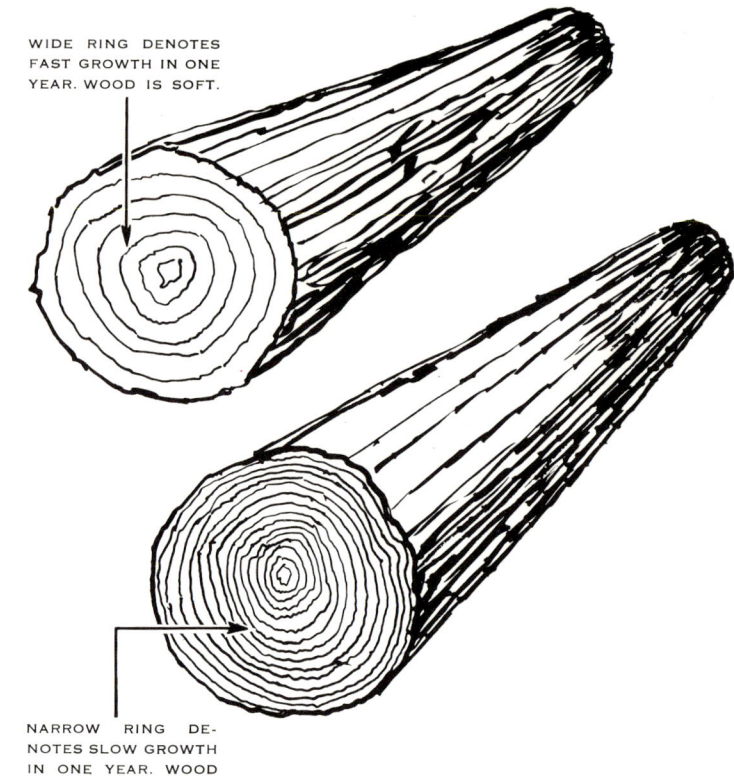

WIDE RING DENOTES FAST GROWTH IN ONE YEAR. WOOD IS SOFT.

NARROW RING DENOTES SLOW GROWTH IN ONE YEAR. WOOD IS HARD.

Soft maple and *hard* maple are two entirely different species of trees. But in addition to this difference, trees are like some people — the harder their living conditions, the stronger they grow. *Soft* maple grows in temperate or warm areas where the living is easy. The trees grow fast and the wood is soft. *Hard* maple grows in cold climates where the living is difficult. Growth is slow and the wood is hard. You can see the difference by comparing the cross sections of the trunks of soft and hard maple. Each year, a tree lays down a circle of new wood. The faster the growth, the wider each "annual ring." With soft maple, the rings are wide apart and the wood is soft. With hard maple, the rings are close together and the wood is hard. The drawings on this page show the difference. Tell City Young Republic is made of carefully selected, top-grade Hard Rock Maple which is hand-picked for uniform color and freedom from blemishes. *The wood is so hard, it will bend a nail if you attempt to hammer it into the wood without first drilling a hole.*

THE GRAIN IS NATURE'S FINGERPRINT

No two pieces of wood have exactly the same graining, just as no two people have exactly the same fingerprints. This is one of the charms of Young Republic Solid Hard Rock Maple since each piece of the furniture has a pleasing variation of grain patterns.

...and there's a difference in finishes

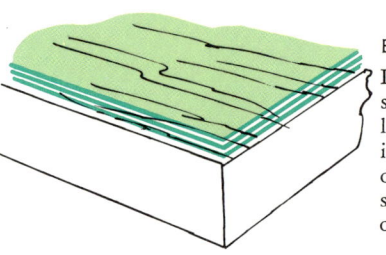

BUILT-UP FINISH
Layer after layer is built up into a smooth, glassy finish. It is brittle, like glass, and chips easily. The finish lies on top of the wood like layers of microscopically thin glass. It obscures the grain and hides the beauty of the wood.

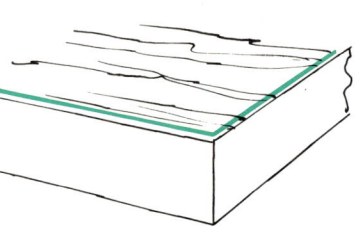

YOUNG REPUBLIC CLEAR FINISH
Actually penetrates the wood and becomes part of it! Because it is clear, the natural beauty of the grain shows through. Its soft lustre gives permanent protection but is easy to maintain.

The room setting above features the No. F-8152 Pedestal Table with two No. 8037 Ladderback Arm Chairs and two No. 8036 Ladderback Side Chairs. The Hutch is our No. 8392/8393 Buffet-Hutch. Shown at right is the No. F-829 Wheeled Server.

Informality is conveyed in this dining room by the use of inside shutters and short café curtains. This treatment takes advantage of the fine view and accents the deep reveal of the windows. Its color scheme is as Yankee as our flag and calls attention to the provincial detailing of the front door. The large hutch provides plenty of storage space for linen and silver as well as displaying decorative objects. Note the rough-sawn timbers and beams as well as the practical brick floor with its many coats of wax. The center fixture began life holding pans in a kitchen and now suspends four small black lanterns fitted with candles. The tin whale once reported the direction of the wind atop a New England fisherman's cottage. He looks as if he could be easily duplicated with a pair of tin snips. While this dining table lends a feeling of intimacy in its present position, it can expand to seat eight.

Solid hard rock maple
DINING ROOM

DINING TABLES

Gracious dining begins with the dining table itself. Around this table go the chairs which lend individuality and charm to the dining area. Add buffets, hutches and serving pieces from the Young Republic Group and you have a "picture pretty" dining room.

To start your dining room, Tell City offers dining tables in a variety of styles and sizes to fit any family. On these pages and those which follow you will find illustrations of all types of tables—round, oval, drop-leaf, extension, pedestal or trestle—many surfaced with Formica® brand laminated plastic.

Legs and bases are made of carefully selected hard rock maple, generously proportioned to assure solid support.

No. 8174 Extension Table. Made of Solid Hard Rock Maple in #48 Andover finish. Diameter 48" closed. Extends to 68" with 2 leaves.

No. 8174-S with Spoon Foot Leg.

No. 8161 Drop Leaf Extension Table. Shown with **No. 8166 Lazy Susan.** Made of Solid Hard Rock Maple in #48 Andover finish. Diameter 48" with drop leaves up. Top 48" x 24" with drop leaves down. Extends to 68" with 2 leaves. Separate Lazy Susan, 20" diameter.

No. 8161-S with Spoon Foot Leg.

No. 8151-S Drop Leaf Extension Table with Spoon Foot Leg. Made of Solid Hard Rock Maple in #48 Andover finish. Diameter 48" with drop leaves up. Top 48" x 24" with drop leaves down. Extends to 88" with 4 leaves.

No. 8151 with Turned Leg.

Dining room group illustrated at left includes the 8156X2 Oval Extension Table with 8038 Side Chairs, 8039 Arm Chairs, 8388/8390 Buffet-Hutch and F-829 Wheeled Server.

No. 8165 Gateleg Extension Table. Made of Solid Hard Rock Maple in #48 Andover finish. Top closed 44" x 27". With leaves up 44" x 69". Extends to 90" with 2 leaves.

No. 8156X2 Oval Extension Table. Made of Solid Hard Rock Maple in #48 Andover finish. Top 42" x 60" when closed. Extends to 84" with 2 aproned leaves.

No. 8156X3 Extends to 96" with 3 aproned leaves.

tops surfaced with FORMICA BRAND laminated plastic

Rub your hand over these tables surfaced with a new type of Formica® brand laminated plastic and you will find that they even look and feel like wood. The finish is not shiny like other plastic tops and more closely matches the grain and soft finish of natural maple. And this new surface does not show streaks or hairline scratches like the old shiny kind. Yet these tops are incredibly durable and are particularly suited to families with small children. They are a blessing to those who use the dining table for games, homework, sewing and other activities that could mar an ordinary surface. Tables surfaced with Formica® brand laminated plastic are indispensable for the kitchen or family room, and practical in the dining room as well.

No. F-8178 Harvest Table. Base made of Solid Hard Rock Maple in #48 Andover finish. FORMICA top, maple grain. Top with leaves down 60″ x 20″. With leaves up 60″ x 38″.

No. F-821 Table. Base made of Solid Hard Rock Maple in #48 Andover finish. With FORMICA top. Legs pull out to support drop leaves. With leaves down 34″ x 16″. With leaves up 34″ x 34″. Height 28½″.

No. F-8176X2 Drop Leaf Extension Table. Base made of Solid Hard Rock Maple in #48 Andover finish. FORMICA top, maple grain. Top closed 40″ x 25″. With leaves up 40″ x 58″. Extends to 78″ with 2 leaves.

No. F-8176X2-S with Spoon Foot Leg.

No. F-8176X4 Table extends to 98″ with 4 leaves

No. F-8176X4-S with Spoon Foot Leg.

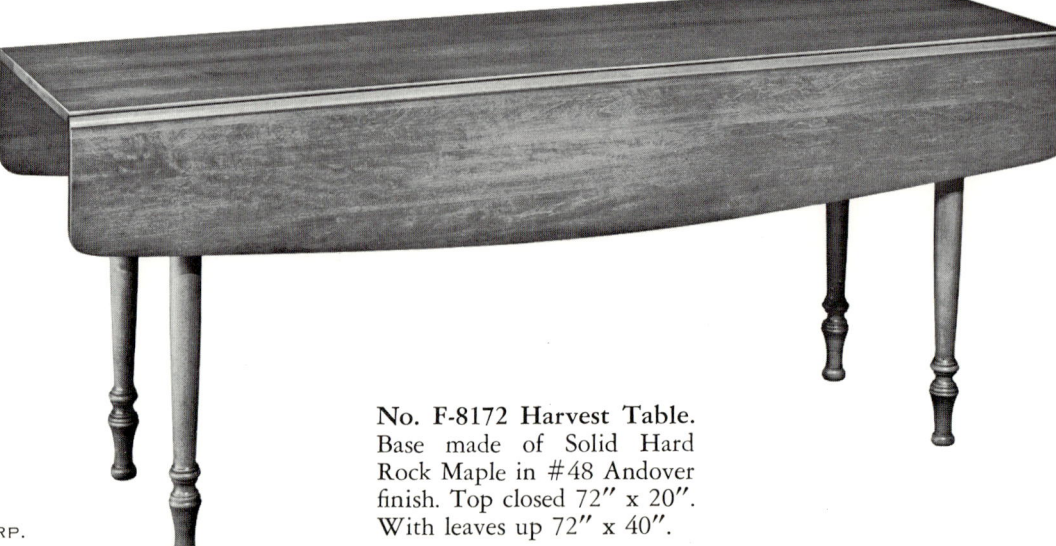

No. F-8172 Harvest Table. Base made of Solid Hard Rock Maple in #48 Andover finish. Top closed 72″ x 20″. With leaves up 72″ x 40″.

tops surfaced with
FORMICA BRAND
laminated plastic

No. F-8161-S Drop Leaf Extension with Spoon Foot Leg. Base made of Solid Hard Rock Maple in #48 Andover finish. FORMICA top, maple grain. With **F-8166** FORMICA top Lazy Susan. Diameter 48″ with drop leaves up. Top 48″ x 24″ with drop leaves down. Extends to 69″ with 2 leaves. Separate Lazy Susan, 20″ diameter.

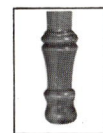 **No. F-8161** with Turned Leg

No. F-8162 Thick Top Drop Leaf Extension Table. Base made of Solid Hard Rock Maple in #48 Andover finish. FORMICA top, maple grain. Diameter 48″ with drop leaves up. Top 48″ x 24″ with drop leaves down. Extends to 69″ with 2 leaves.

No. F-8162-S with Spoon Foot Leg.

Families with children would do well to consider plastic-topped tables. The grain pattern is now so cleverly done, you can hardly tell it from the rest of the solid wood table.

No. F-8151 Drop Leaf Extension Table. Base made of Solid Hard Rock Maple in #48 Andover finish. FORMICA top, maple grain. Diameter 48″ with drop leaves up. Top 48″ x 24″ with drop leaves down. Extends to 90″ with 4 leaves.

No. F-8151-S with Spoon Foot Leg.

No. F-8173 Drop Leaf Extension Table. Base made of Solid Hard Rock Maple in #48 Andover finish. FORMICA top, maple grain. Drop-leaf, 42″ diameter with drop leaves up. With drop leaves down 42″ x 23½″. Extends to 57″ with 1 leaf.

No. F-8173-S with Spoon Foot Leg.

tops surfaced with

FORMICA BRAND

laminated plastic

No. F-8560 Thick Top Extension Table. Base made of Solid Hard Rock Maple in #48 Andover finish. FORMICA top, maple grain. Diameter 42″ closed. Extends to 60″ with 2 leaves.

No. F-8560-S with Spoon Foot Leg.

No. F-8160 Extension Table. Base made of Solid Hard Rock Maple in #48 Andover finish. FORMICA top, maple grain. Diameter 42″ closed. Extends to 60″ with 2 leaves.

No. F-8160-S with Spoon Foot Leg.

No. F-8157 Round Table. Base made of Solid Hard Rock Maple in #48 Andover finish. FORMICA top, Maple finish. Top 42″ diameter.

No. F-8157-S with Spoon Foot Leg.

No. F-8159 Pedestal Extension Table. Base made of Solid Hard Rock Maple in #48 Andover finish. FORMICA top, maple grain. Diameter 42″. Extends to 60″ with 2 aproned leaves.

No. F-8153 Thick Top Extension Table. Base made of Solid Hard Rock Maple in #48 Andover finish. FORMICA top, maple grain. Diameter 48". Extends to 96" with 4 leaves.

No. F-8153-S with Spoon Foot Leg.

No. F-8163 Thick Top Extension Table. Base made of Solid Hard Rock Maple in #48 Andover finish. FORMICA top, maple grain. Diameter 48". Extends to 72" with 2 leaves.

No. F-8163-S with Spoon Foot Leg.

tops surfaced with

laminated plastic

No. F-8152 Pedestal Extension Table. Base made of Solid Hard Rock Maple with laminated skirt. #48 Andover finish. FORMICA top, maple grain. Diameter 48". Extends to 72" with 2 aproned leaves.

No. F-8174 Extension Table. Base made of Solid Hard Rock Maple in #48 Andover finish. FORMICA top, maple grain. Diameter 48" closed. Extends to 72" with 2 leaves.

No. F-8174-S with Spoon Foot Leg.

tops surfaced with

FORMICA BRAND

laminated plastic

No. F-8575X2 Thick Top Extension Table. Base made of Solid Hard Rock Maple in #48 Andover finish. FORMICA top, maple grain. Top 44″ x 66″ when closed. Extends to 90″ with 2 aproned leaves.

No. F-8575X3 extends to 102″ with 3 leaves.

No. F-8155X1 Oval Extension Table. Base made of Solid Hard Rock Maple in #48 Andover finish. FORMICA top, maple grain. Top 36″ x 48″ closed. Extends to 60″ with 1 leaf.

No. F-8155X2 extends to 72″ with 2 leaves.

No. F-8156X2 Oval Extension Table. Base made of Solid Hard Rock Maple in #48 Andover finish. FORMICA top, maple grain. Top 42″ x 60″ when closed. Extends to 84″ with 2 aproned leaves.

No. F-8156X3 extends to 96″ with 3 leaves.

No. F-8154X1 Butterfly Extension Table. Base made of Solid Hard Rock Maple in #48 Andover finish. FORMICA top. Top closed 42″ x 30″. With leaves up 42″ x 72″. Extends to 84″ with 1 leaf.

No. F-8154X2 extends to 96″ with 2 leaves.

No. F-8158 Sawbuck Table. With extra thick top. Base made of Solid Hard Rock Maple in #48 Andover finish. FORMICA top, Maple grain. Top 36″ x 72″.

No. 8041 Sawbuck Bench. Made of Solid Hard Rock Maple in #48 Andover finish. W 60″ D 15″ H 17½″.

tops surfaced with
FORMICA BRAND
laminated plastic

No. F-8564 Trestle Extension Table. Base made of Solid Hard Rock Maple in #48 Andover finish. FORMICA top, Maple grain. Top 36″ x 72″ when closed. Extends to 96″ with 2 leaves.

No. 8040 Trestle Bench. Made of Solid Hard Rock Maple in #48 Andover finish. W 60″ D 15″ H 17½″

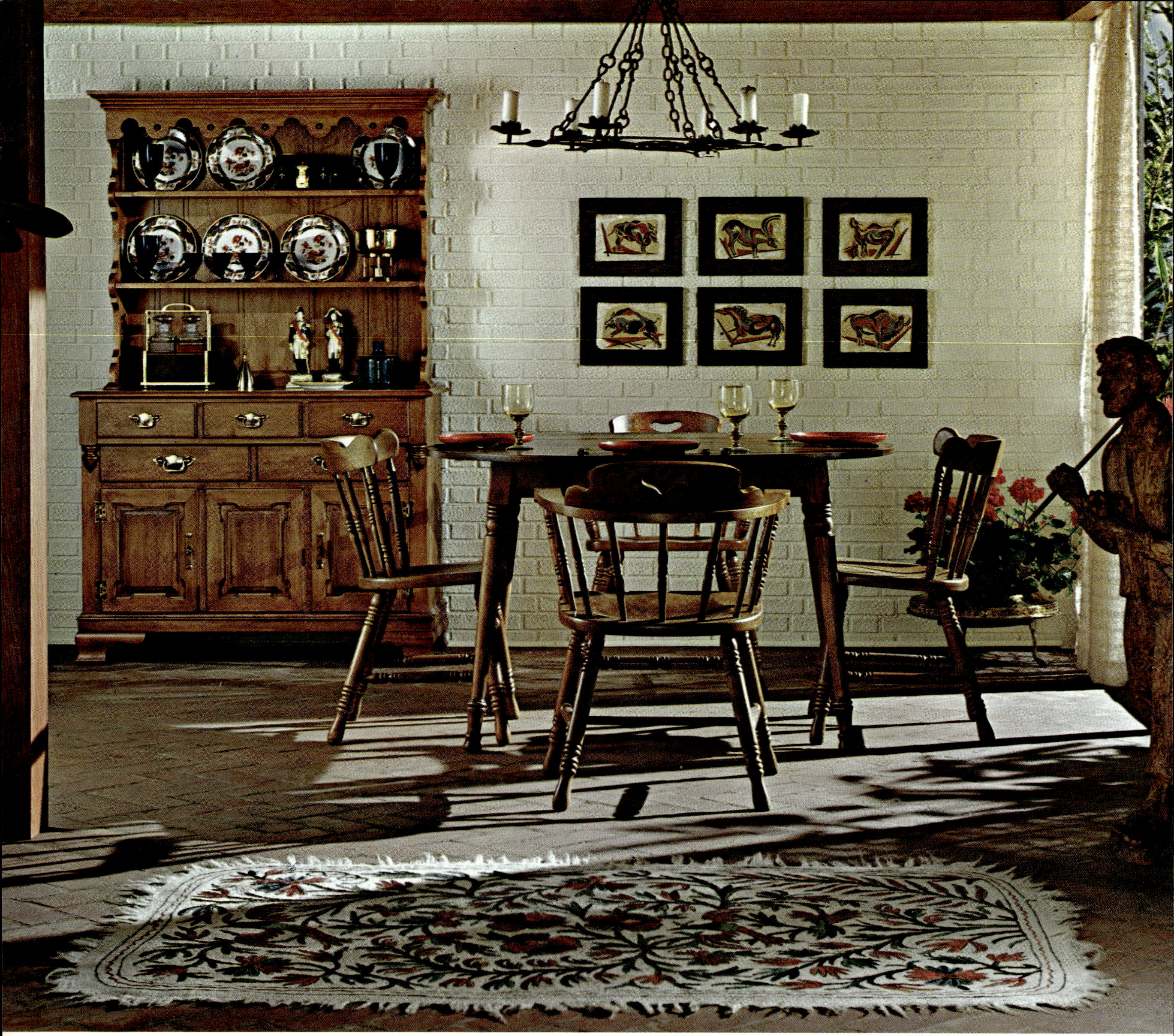

Shown above is the No. 8384/8385 Buffet-Hutch. Table is No. 8161 with two No. 8008 Captain's Chairs and two No. 8018 Mate's Chairs.

The key to the success of this dining room is simplicity and air space. The exposed brick painted white provides an attractive texture with an indoor-outdoor feeling. Plants help, too. The antique wood carving is an interesting touch. If you are lucky enough to find a good example of Early Americana such as this, by all means use it. Even tools or utensils make interesting wall pieces if they silhouette well.

TELL CITY CHAIRS®
are styled for beauty and lasting comfort

Over the past century, more than 30 million chairs have been produced by the fine craftsmen at Tell City. Many of these chairs are still in use—because they are made to last.

For example, all back slats are steam-bent so they will fit comfortably. Back posts and arm stumps on all chairs are driven all the way through the seat and wedged from the bottom so the arms and back stay tight permanently. Wooden seats are unusually thick and have comfortable saddles. And when you look at the underconstruction, you'll find sturdy legs with more than the usual number of stretchers to assure lasting rigidity.

No. 8008 Captain's Chair. Made of Solid Hard Rock Maple in #48 Andover finish. Seat: 19" wide, 15½" deep. Over-all: W 24" D 21½" H 30¾".

No. 8018 Mate's Chair. Made of Solid Hard Rock Maple in #48 Andover finish. Seat: 17" wide, 13¾" deep. Over-all: W 21" D 20½" H. 31".

No. 8046 Mate's Chair. Made of Solid Hard Rock Maple in #48 Andover finish. Seat: 18" wide, 15" deep. Over-all: W 21" D 21" H 32½".

No. 8047 Captain's Chair. Made of Solid Hard Rock Maple in #48 Andover finish. Seat: 21" wide, 16" deep. Over-all: W 25¾" D 22½" H 31".

No. 8048 Side Chair. Made of Solid Hard Rock Maple in #48 Andover finish. Seat 17½" wide, 14½" deep. Over-all: W 19¾" D 22" H 36½".

No. 8049 Arm Chair. Made of Solid Hard Rock Maple in #48 Andover finish. Seat 20½" wide, 15¾" deep. Over-all: W 25¾" D 22¾" H 36½".

No. 8026 Thumb Back Side Chair. Made of Solid Hard Rock Maple in #48 Andover finish. Seat: 16½" wide, 14½" deep. Over-all: W 19" D 20¾" H 34¼".

"CHAIRS CAN CHANGE THE ENTIRE FEELING OF A ROOM"

No. 8052 Duxbury Side Chair. Made of Solid Hard Rock Maple in #48 Andover finish. Seat 17" wide, 16" deep. Over-all: W 25½" D 21¼" H 37½".

No. 8053 Duxbury Arm Chair. Made of Solid Hard Rock Maple in #48 Andover finish. Seat: 19¾" wide, 16¾" deep. Over-all: W 26¼" D 23¼" H 37½".

No. 8038 Slip Seat Side Chair. Made of Solid Hard Rock Maple in #48 Andover finish. Seat: 18" wide, 16" deep. Over-all: W 19¼" D 23½" H 39½".

No. 8027 Thumb Back Arm Chair. Made of Solid Hard Rock Maple in #48 Andover finish. Seat: 19¼" wide, 15½" deep. Over-all: W 22¾" D 21¼" H 34¼".

No. D-8026 Thumb Back Side Chair. Made of Solid Hard Rock Maple in #75 Black and Gold or #74 Andover and Gold. Seat: 16½" wide, 14½" deep. Over-all: W 19" D 20¾" H 34¼".

No. D-8027 Thumb Back Arm Chair. Made of Solid Hard Rock Maple in #75 Black and Gold or #74 Andover and Gold. Seat: 19¼" wide, 15½" deep. Over-all: W 22¾" D 21¼" H 34¼".

Your choice of chairs in a dining area actually establishes the character of the room. Take a round table and see how it changes when you try a set of high Ladderbacks, four squat heavy Captain's Chairs or Black-and-Gold Hitchcock Chairs. With the long line of Tell City Chairs, you have infinite variety to express your own individuality.

No. 8039 Slip Seat Arm Chair. Made of Solid Hard Rock Maple in #48 Andover finish. Seat: 21" wide, 16¼" deep. Over-all: W 24" D 26½" H 45½".

No. 8036 Ladderback Side Chair. Made of Solid Hard Rock Maple in #48 Andover finish. Seat: 17½" wide, 14¼" deep. Over-all: W 19" D 22¼" H 44¾".

No. 8037 Ladderback Arm Chair. Made of Solid Hard Rock Maple in #48 Andover finish. Seat: 19½" wide, 15¼" deep. Over-all: W 25½" D 23¾" H 44¾".

Just as you use lipstick to add brightness and charm to your smile, these hand-glazed chairs in lovely antiqued colored finishes can add gaiety and brightness to your Early American home.

Be bold in your use of these chairs. Use them in sets of one color, or mix with mellow, natural Andover Maple finish to achieve unusual table settings.

All chairs illustrated above are available in a choice of four finishes—Antique Blue, Antique Green, Antique Red and Antique Yellow.

Descriptive Information:

No. A-2202 Farmhouse Chair	Page 28
No. A-8033 Ladderback Arm Chair	Page 27
No. A-8034 Cattail Side Chair	Page 27
No. A-8032 Ladderback Side Chair	Page 27
No. A-8035 Cattail Arm Chair	Page 27

TELL CITY CHAIR COMPANY
TELL CITY, IND.

No. 8034 Cattail Chair. Made of Solid Hard Rock Maple in #48 Andover finish. Seat: 18″ wide, 15¾″ deep. Over-all: W 19¾″ D 23″ H 38″.

No. A-8034 in #86 Antique Blue, #87 Antique Green, #88 Antique Red or #89 Antique Yellow finish.

No. 8035 Cattail Arm Chair. Made of Solid Hard Rock Maple in #48 Andover finish. Seat 21″ wide, 16¾″ deep. Over-all: W 26″ D 25″ H 38″.

No. A-8035 in #86 Antique Blue, #87 Antique Green, #88 Antique Red or #89 Antique Yellow finish.

No. 8032 Ladderback Chair. Made of Solid Hard Rock Maple in #48 Andover finish. Seat: 17″ wide, 15½″ deep. Over-all: W 19¼″ D 21″ H 37¼″.

No. A-8032 in #86 Antique Blue, #87 Antique Green, #88 Antique Red or #89 Antique Yellow finish.

No. 8033 Ladderback Arm Chair. Made of Solid Hard Rock Maple in #48 Andover finish. Seat: 19½″ wide, 16″ deep. Over-all: W 23¾″ D 22¼″ H 37¼″.

No. A-8033 in #86 Antique Blue, #87 Antique Green, #88 Antique Red or #89 Antique Yellow finish.

Decorated and Antique color finishes provide you many opportunities to design a dining area that reflects your individual taste.

No. 8042 Ladderback Side Chair. Made of Solid Hard Rock Maple in #48 Andover finish. Fibre seat. Seat: 19¼″ wide, 15¾″ deep. Over-all: W 19¼″ D 19″ H 41¾″.

No. 8043 Ladderback Arm Chair. Made of Solid Hard Rock Maple in #48 Andover finish. Fibre seat. Seat: 21″ wide, 17¼″ deep. Over-all: W 21½″ D 22¾″ H 41¾″.

Early American Chairs
IN SELECTED HARDWOODS

No. D-2312 Ladderback Side Chair. Fibre seat. Made of Selected Hardwoods. Decorated in #75 Black and Gold. Seat: 18" wide, 14¾" deep. Over-all: W 18½" D 18½" H 40¾".

No. D-2313 Ladderback Arm Chair. Fibre seat. Made of Selected Hardwoods. Decorated in #75 Black and Gold. Seat: 21" wide, 16½" deep. Over-all: W 21¼" D 21¾" H 40¾".

No. 2202 Farm House Chair. Made of Selected Hardwoods in #48 Andover Maple finish. Seat: 14¾" wide, 13" deep. Over-all: W 17½" D 18½" H 33".

No. D-2202 in #74 Andover and Gold.

No. A-2202 in #86 Antique Blue, #87 Antique Green, #88 Antique Red or #89 Antique Yellow finish.

No. D-2270 Hitchcock Side Chair. Fibre seat. Made of Selected Hardwoods. Decorated in #75 Black and Gold and #74 Andover and Gold. Seat: 17½" wide, 15½" deep. Over-all: W 18¼" D 19¼" H 34½".

No. W-2270 in #72 White and Gold.

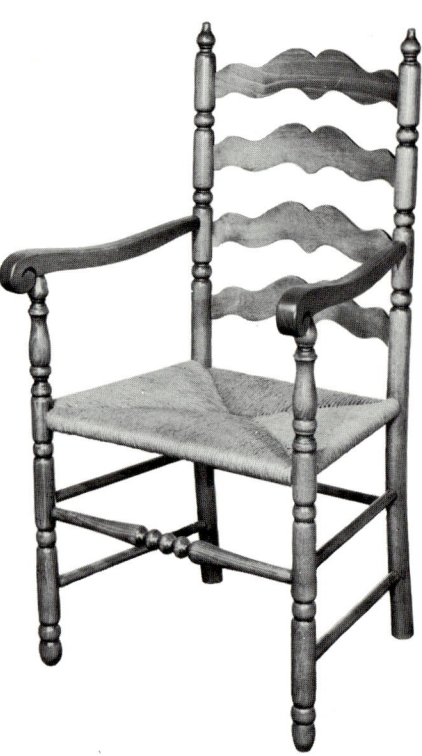

No. 2270 Hitchcock Side Chair. Fibre seat. Made of Selected Hardwoods in #48 Andover Maple finish. Seat: 17½" wide, 15½" deep. Over-all: W 18¼" D 19¼" H 34½".

No. 2312 Ladderback Side Chair. Fibre seat. Made of Selected Hardwoods in choice of #27 Mahogany finish, #30 Walnut finish, #48 Andover Maple finish or #95 Cherry finish. Seat: 18" wide, 14¾" deep. Over-all: W 18½" D 18½" H 40¾".

No. 2313 Ladderback Arm Chair. Fibre seat. Made of Selected Hardwoods in choice of #27 Mahogany finish, #30 Walnut finish, #48 Andover Maple finish or #95 Cherry finish. Seat: 21" wide, 16½" deep. Over-all: W 21¼" D 21¾" H 40¾".

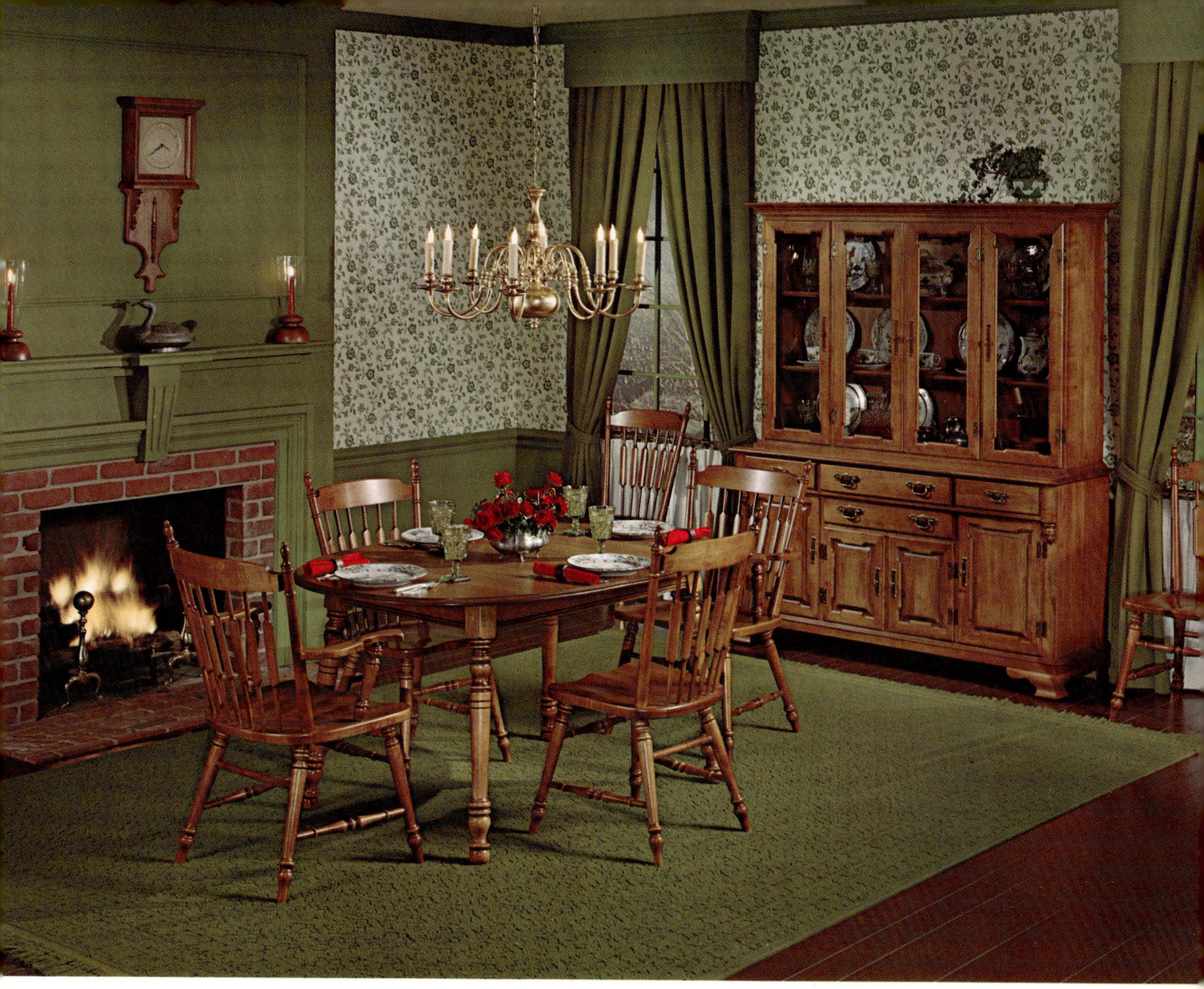

The dining group above includes the No. 8392/8395 Buffet-Hutch, No. F-8156X3 Oval Extension Table, No. 8034 Cattail Chairs and No. 8035 Cattail Arm Chairs. Hanging above the fireplace is No. 3143 Wall Clock.

Gracious dining in the traditional manner is exemplified by this dining scene. A monochromatic color scheme was selected, with a rich Williamsburg green for the woodwork, carpet and window drapes. Above a painted wainscot is a figured flower pattern wallpaper with a green overtone that harmonizes well with the painted mantel and general color theme. The wood floor is stained dark brown to border the green area rug. The cool color of walls, draperies and rug complements the warm tones of the furniture. Note the added sparkle attained with red accents.

For soft illumination of the dining table, the decorator selected a gleaming brass chandelier with simulated candleholders in true Early American styling.

The oval table may be expanded to seat eight guests and the commodious 60″ buffet-hutch provides a good display for cherished dinnerware and antique glassware.

This is a room that ideally illustrates the warmth and hospitality so closely associated with good Early American furniture and tasteful choice of colors and accessories.

29

Get exact combination of features you want

The 44"-wide buffet illustrated on page 31 makes a handsome serving and storage piece. It can be used as a base for one of the three different hutch tops on page 31 to achieve the exact combination of features you want. The open hutch has a unique slotted spoon rack on the top shelf. Partially closed hutch has a plate gallery and two hinged compartments with decorative wire grills. The doors on the cupboard close off storage area behind glass and repeat the corner design motif of the buffet doors. The smaller 36" wide buffet-hutches at left fit nicely into a limited area. The corner cupboard takes even less floor space, extending only about a foot and a half into the room.

No. 8380/8383 Buffet-Hutch. With one drawer in base. Made of Solid Hard Rock Maple in #48 Andover finish. W 36" D 19" H 69¾".

SILVER DRAWER IN ALL BUFFETS

A felt-lined silver drawer with convenient partitions is a feature of all Tell City buffets and buffet-hutches.

No. 8380/8399 Buffet-Hutch. With one drawer in base. Made of Solid Hard Rock Maple in #48 Andover finish. W 36" D 19" H 69¼".

No. 8387 Corner Cupboard. Made of Solid Hard Rock Maple in #48 Andover finish. W 34" D 19¼" H 70".

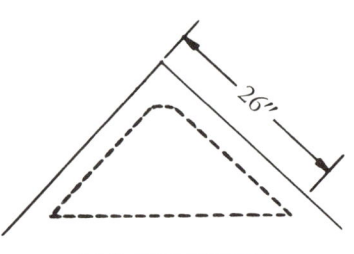

WALL SPACE REQUIRED

No. 8384/8385 Buffet-Hutch. With four drawers. Made of Solid Hard Rock Maple in #48 Andover finish. W 44″ D 19″ H 70″.

No. 8384/8398 Buffet-Hutch. With four drawers in base. Made of Solid Hard Rock Maple in #48 Andover finish. W 44″ D 19″ H 70″.

No. 8384/8386 Buffet-Hutch. With four drawers. Made of Solid Hard Rock Maple in #48 Andover finish. W 44″ D 19″ H 70″.

No. 8384 Buffet. With four drawers. Made of Solid Hard Rock Maple in #48 Andover finish. W 44″ D 19″ H 33″.

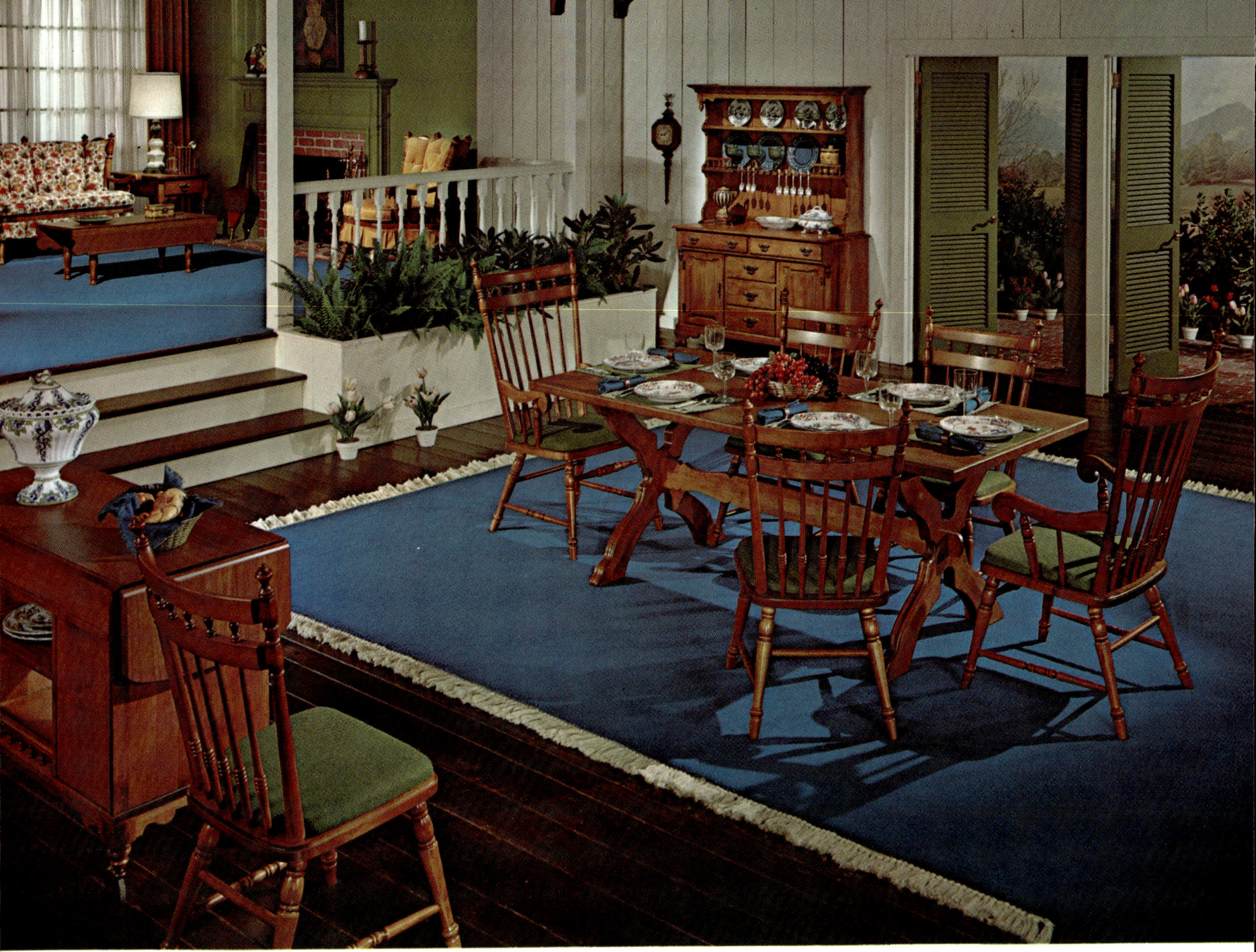

Dining Table illustrated is No. F-8158 Sawbuck Table. Chairs are No. 8038 and No. 8039 Slip Seat patterns. Wheeled server in foreground is No. F-829. Buffet-Hutch is No. 8388/8389. Living area features No. 8203 Sofa, No. 8200 Wing Rocker, No. F-8412 Cocktail Table and No. F-8410 End Table. Accessories include No. 3162 Lantern Clock.

Early American furniture is well adapted to bi-level or split-level contemporary homes like the illustration above.

For the dining area, we selected a Formica topped sawbuck table and slip seat chairs with rough-textured seat covers for color accent. The wheeled server in the foreground is handily available for buffet-style serving. On the far wall a 52″ open hutch offers decorative display of antique spoons, colorful dinner plates and antique glass. To accentuate the warm blue area rug with its white fringe, the wooden plank floor has been given a dark stain.

The blue of the area rug has been extended to the living area, tying the two levels together. For more coordination, the wall surrounding the fireplace is painted a deep green to match the dining room shutters. Stained decorative beams are offset by whitewashed barn siding.

A brightly patterned sofa and solid color upholstered chair add color to the living area and complete our popular color scheme of blues, greens, and golds. Lacy ferns, rhododendrons and pots of tulips soften the planter and form an attractive, yet open, room divider.

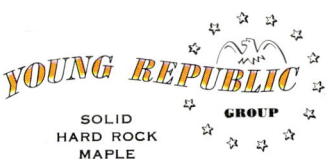

An open and closed version of the popular 52" Hutch

There is real storage room in the closed cupboard and the attractive glass doors afford protection from dust.

The open hutch has plate grooves and two gallery rails, plus an unusual and attractive spoon rack.

The five drawer base offers a felt-lined silver drawer and two large storage compartments. All doors have magnetic catches and raised panel centers.

No. 8388/8390 Buffet-Hutch. With five drawers. Made of Solid Hard Rock Maple in #48 Andover finish. W 52" D 19" H 71".

No. 8388/8389 Buffet-Hutch. With five drawers. Made of Solid Hard Rock Maple in #48 Andover finish. W 52" D 19" H 72".

No. 8388 Buffet. With five drawers. Made of Solid Hard Rock Maple in #48 Andover finish. W 52" D 19" H 33".

A Buffet, Hutch and China in 60" width

No. 8392 Buffet. With four drawers. Made of Solid Hard Rock Maple in #48 Andover finish. W 60" D 19" H 33".

No. 8392/8395 Buffet-Hutch. With four drawers in base. Made of Solid Hard Rock Maple in #48 Andover finish. W 60" D 19" H 74".

No. 8392/8393 Buffet-Hutch. With four drawers. Made of Solid Hard Rock Maple in #48 Andover finish. W 60" D 19" H 75".

48" Closed China with Crown Glass Front

A Variety of Styles for Display, Storage and Efficient Serving

This China was designed to display your most cherished collection of dinnerware and glass in the rich setting it deserves. The curved crown glass gives added luster to your possessions and shows them off to their best advantage. Ample storage beneath, too!

If space is limited, the 37″ wheeled server extends to 53½″ with drop leaves up. Its Formica brand laminated plastic top makes a thoroughly practical surface for buffet or bar service—and it can be wheeled about. The dry sink also has a Formica serving top and a virtually indestructible copper tray for beverage service or planting.

No. 8370/8372 China. With Crown glass. Made of Solid Hard Rock Maple in #48 Andover finish. W 48″ D 16″ H 71″.

No. 8380 Server. With one drawer. Made of Solid Hard Rock Maple in #48 Andover finish. W 36″ D 19″ H 33″.

No. 828 Dry Sink. Made of Solid Hard Rock Maple in #48 Andover finish. Copper tray. FORMICA serving top. W 38″ D 18″ H 33″.

No. F-829 Wheeled Server. With two drawers. Made of Solid Hard Rock Maple in #48 Andover finish. FORMICA top, height 31″. With leaves down 37″ x 18″. With leaves up 53½″ x 18″.

No. 8312 Triple Dresser illustrated has centered Mirror No. 8313. No. 8142 Chairback Bed is shown. At right is No. 8302 Chest. Seen in adjoining room is the No. 8303 Tallboy Chest. By the bed is No. A-2202 Farmhouse Chair. Two No. 8311 Night Tables flank bed. No. 8252 Love Seat is in foreground. Accessories illustrated include No. 3163 Magazine Rack, No. A-3166 Wag Clock, No. 2231 Oval Footstool, No. 3146 Treasure Chest, No. 3123 Corner Whatnot, No. 3115 Hat Tree and No. A-3165 Octagon Mirror. No. A-3321/5539 Table Lamp is shown on dresser and a pair of No. A-3322/5540 Table Lamps on Night Tables.

This "dream" bedroom typifies the warmth and livability that can be obtained with Early American furniture. The skylight highlights the cool green of the bed alcove which harmonizes with the warm ochre of the adjoining walls. An olive wall-to-wall carpet makes a softly muted setting for the scene, accented by a colorful throw rug in front of the dresser. Matching drapes and bed cover add a bright pattern to the room. Carefully selected groupings of colored wall accessories relieve the monochromatic background. Wooden uprights in a dark natural stain add height to the room and frame the window. Note the pleasing effect and privacy attained with the café curtain. The chair and love seat provide practical seating and add to the "lived-in" appearance of the room. All in all, this is a bedroom that invites reading, resting, and complete relaxation.

SOLID HARD ROCK MAPLE

BEDROOM

No. 8312 Triple Dresser. With 12 drawers (2 concealed behind doors). Made of Solid Hard Rock Maple in #48 Andover finish. W 66" D 20" H 33".

No. 8313 Mirror. Made of Solid Hard Rock Maple in #48 Andover finish. Plate 34" x 26". Sold separately.

ALL CHESTS AND DRESSERS AVAILABLE WITH CASTERS

Changing the Mood with Mirrors

An artful selection of the proper mirror—or mirrors—can change the entire look of a dresser and set the mood for the complete bedroom.

Shown here are a variety of combinations utilizing one of Tell City's Triple Dressers.

No. 8312 Triple Dresser. Shown with No. 8308 Mirror. (Mirror described on page 38.)

No. 8312 Triple Dresser. Shown with 2 No. 3176 Mirrors. (Mirrors described on page 40.)

No. 8312 Triple Dresser. Shown with 2 No. 8319 Mirrors. (Mirrors described on page 40.)

A 60" Dresser with plenty of drawer space

No. 8307 Triple Dresser. With 11 drawers. Made of Solid Hard Rock Maple in #48 Andover finish. W 60" D 19" H 33".

No. 8308 Mirror. Plate 44" x 28". Sold separately.

No. 8307 Triple Dresser. Shown with 2 No. 3176 Mirrors. (Mirrors described on page 40.)

ALL CHESTS AND DRESSERS AVAILABLE WITH CASTERS

No. 8307 Triple Dresser. Shown with No. 8313 Mirror. (Mirror described on page 37.)

No. 8307 Triple Dresser. Shown with 2 No. 8319 Mirrors. (Mirrors described on page 40.)

A Compact 54" Dresser with Eight Drawers

No. 8305 Double Dresser.
Shown with No. 3176 Mirror.
(Mirror described on page 40.)

No. 8305 Double Dresser.
Shown with No. 8313 Mirror.
(Mirror described on page 37.)

No. 8305 Double Dresser. With 8 drawers. Made of Solid Hard Rack Maple in #48 Andover finish. W 54" D 19" H 33".

No. 8306 Mirror. Plate 38" x 28". Sold separately.

No. 8305 Double Dresser.
Shown with No. 8319 Mirror.
(Mirror described on page 40.)

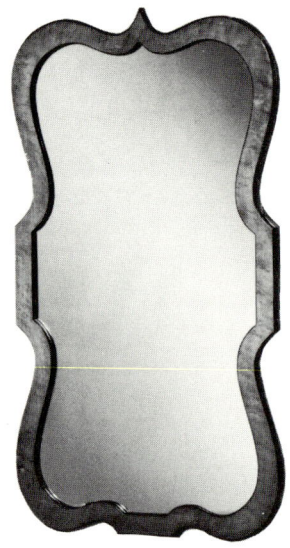

No. 3176 Fancy Mirror.
Veneered frame trimmed in Black. Bird's-Eye Maple face. Plate 20″ x 38″. Over-all: W 22½″ D 1″ H 41½″.

No. D-8309 Standing Swivel Decorated Mirror. Decorated in #74 Andover and Gold finish. Features scooped trough on base for hairpins, change, etc. Over-all: 20″ x 16½″.

No. 8309 Standing Swivel Mirror. Made of Solid Hard Rock Maple in #48 Andover finish.

No. 878 Vanity.
With 1 drawer. Made of Solid Hard Rock Maple in #48 Andover finish. W 32½″ D 18″ H 29¾″.
Shown with No. D-8309 Swivel Mirror.

The bedroom is the most intimate of rooms so it should reflect your own interests more than any other room. Here is the best place for your personal color preferences.

No. F-8317 Dressing Table.
Base made of Solid Hard Rock Maple in #48 Andover finish. FORMICA top, Maple grain. W 42″ D 19″ H 30″. Mirror 14″ x 13″. Three drawers.

No. 8319 Mirror.
Made of Solid Hard Rock Maple in #48 Andover finish. Plate 20″ x 36″.
Over-all: W 24½″ D 3¾″ H 45″.

The charm of a Young Republic Bedroom comes from its authentic styling and honest craftsmanship

The restful character of Tell City bedroom furniture traces back to our Colonial forefathers. In these patterns you will find the ample proportions and solid craftsmanship that spell enduring quality.

All drawers have dovetailed corners. Insides are sanded smooth to prevent snagging. Center guides insure easy opening and closing. Dust panels keep your clothes clean. These and dozens of other small details mark the work of the furniture craftsmen at Tell City who have been making fine furniture for over 100 years.

No. 8301 Chest-on-Chest. With 6 drawers. Made of Solid Hard Rock Maple in #48 Andover finish. W 36" D 19" H 49".

ALL CHESTS AND DRESSERS AVAILABLE WITH CASTERS.

No. 8300 Chest. With 5 drawers. Made of Solid Hard Rock Maple in #48 Andover finish. W 35" D 19" H 43".

No. 8302 Chest. With 10 drawers. Made of Solid Hard Rock Maple in #48 Andover finish. W 42" D 20" H 42".

No. 8303 Tallboy. With 7 drawers. Made of Solid Hard Rock Maple in #48 Andover finish. W 25" D 17" H 53½".

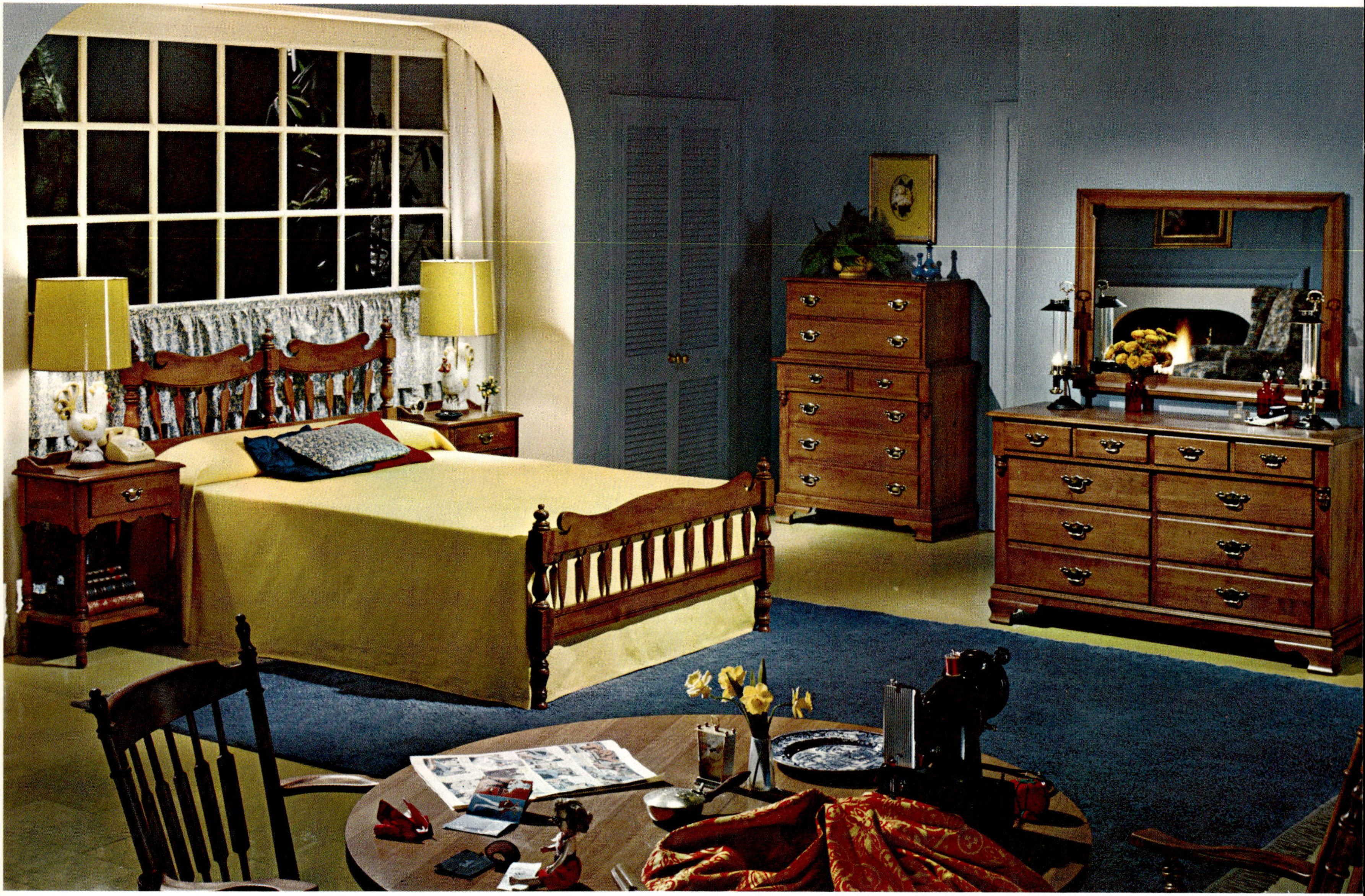

This delightful bedroom features a No. 8118 Chairback Bed with two No. 8121 Night Tables. The chest is our No. 8301 Chest-on-Chest. Completing the group is a No. 8305 Double Dresser with No. 8306 Mirror. In the foreground is a No. F-8163 Round Table and two No. 8035 Cattail Arm Chairs.

A table is a welcome addition to a bedroom whenever space permits. Besides providing a work area, it makes a perfect place for a private Sunday breakfast. Here we see the bed placed in front of a large window. Draperies can be drawn to darken the room and ventilation is provided by auxiliary windows opposite the bed in order to avoid drafts. Storage closets are concealed behind louvered doors allowing ventilation. This is particularly advantageous in damp climates.

No. 8121 Night Table. With 1 drawer. Made of Solid Hard Rock Maple in #48 Andover finish. W 19″ D 15″ H 27″.

No. 8311 Night Stand. With 1 drawer. Made of Solid Hard Rock Maple in #48 Andover finish. W 21″ D 14¾″ H 25″.

No. 8127 Poster Bed 4/6 Double Size. Made of Solid Hard Rock Maple in #48 Andover finish. With #324 Canopy Frame made of aluminum tubing. Posts 69″ high.

Plan the Bedroom Around the Bed!

Since the most important piece of furniture in the bedroom is the bed, it makes sense to be certain that your bed is well designed and soundly constructed.

These beds are constructed with typical Tell City thoroughness. Posts are solid and all joints on footboards and headboards are carefully doweled. Turnings are crisp and clean and sideboards are strong and well blocked.

A pleasing variety of styles is offered in a choice of Twin, Double, Queen and King sizes. Headboard patterns are shown on pages 46 and 47.

No. 8148 Arrowback Bed 4/6. Double Size. Made of Solid Hard Rock Maple in #48 Andover finish. Head Post 44½" high, Foot 28".

No. 8142 Chairback Bed 4/6. Double Size. Head Post 44¾" high, Foot 27¼".

No. 8141 Chairback Bed 5/0. Queen Size. Made of Solid Hard Rock Maple in #48 Andover finish. Head Post 44¾" high, Foot 27¼".

No. 8114 Spindle Bed 4/6 Double Size. Made of Solid Hard Rock Maple in #48 Andover finish. Head Post 39" high, Foot 27".

No. 8115 Spindle Bed 3/3 Twin Size. Head Post 39" high, Foot 27".

Since the bed is the largest unit in the bedroom, place it first and build your designing around it.

No. 8118 Chairback Bed. 4/6 Double Size. Made of Solid Hard Rock Maple in #48 Andover finish. Head Post 44½", Foot 27".

No. 8129 Chairback Bed. 5/0 Queen Size.

No. 8119 Chairback Bed. 3/3 Twin Size.

HEADBOARDS

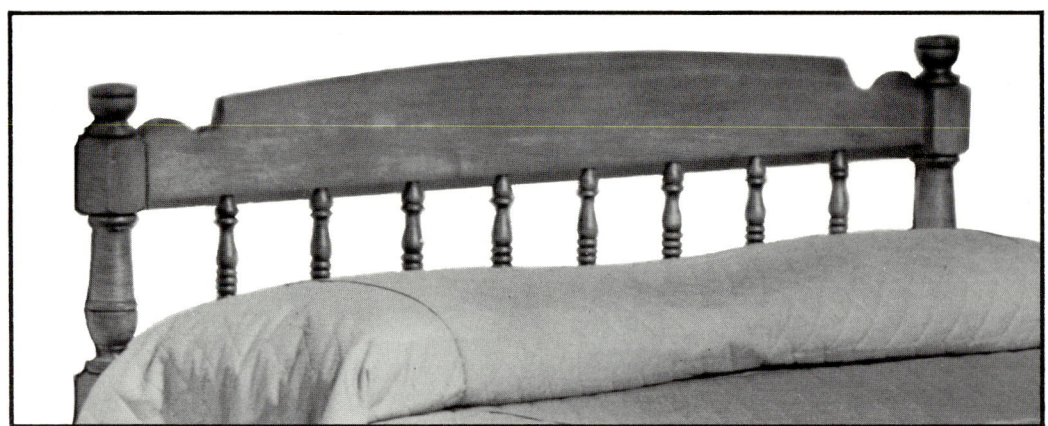

3/3 IS TWIN SIZE
4/6 IS DOUBLE SIZE
5/0 IS QUEEN SIZE

No. 8114-H Spindle Headboard 4/6

No. 8115-H Spindle Headboard 3/3
Made of Solid Hard Rock Maple in #48 Andover finish. Post 39" high.

No. 8141-H Chairback Headboard 5/0

No. 8142-H Chairback Headboard 4/6
Made of Solid Hard Rock Maple in #48 Andover finish. Post 44¾" high.

No. 8118-H Chairback Headboard 4/6

No. 8129-H Chairback Headboard 5/0

No. 8119-H Chairback Headboard 3/3
Made of Solid Hard Rock Maple in #48 Andover finish. Post 44½" high.

If you prefer a Hollywood bed, you can still retain the Early American feeling by selecting a suitable headboard. The Hollywood bed by the absence of a footboard has the advantage of making a small room look larger.

The Sofa in this living room is No. 8253. Upholstered Chair is No. 8234. Lamp Tables are No. 8451 and No. 8420. No. F-8438 Cocktail Table has Formica brand laminated plastic top. Knee-hole Desk in foreground is No. 875, Desk Chair is No. A-2202. With back to camera is No. D-698 Cushioned Boston Rocker with No. 8240 Ottoman. In raised entryway is No. 826 Hall Commode. Accessories include No. 3108 Candlestick on commode, No. 3144 Planter Clock above sofa, No. 3325/5543 Table Lamp and No. 844 Magazine Rack. Cloverleaf Floor Lamp is No. 3360/5534.

A few bright touches of dazzling blue highlight the soft tones of this pleasant living area. Setting off the warm wood finishes is a neutral wall-to-wall carpet. The horizontal lines of the plate rail join with wooden uprights and railing to break up the overall wall tone of warm yellow. Woodwork is painted a creamy white to complement the wall tones. The sofa has a solid color cover slightly lighter and brighter than the wall. Upholstered chair has a crisply checked cover in brown and yellow which is picked up in the versatile ottoman. An interesting accent is the high curio shelf with its bright blue base which matches the blue of the steps. At the right of the stairs is a handsomely stencilled milk container which makes an unusual umbrella rack. This room emphasizes the fact that decorating an Early American room can be easy and relatively inexpensive, limited only by the imagination and daring of the homemaker.

YOUNG REPUBLIC GROUP
SOLID HARD ROCK MAPLE

LIVING ROOM and DINING ROOM

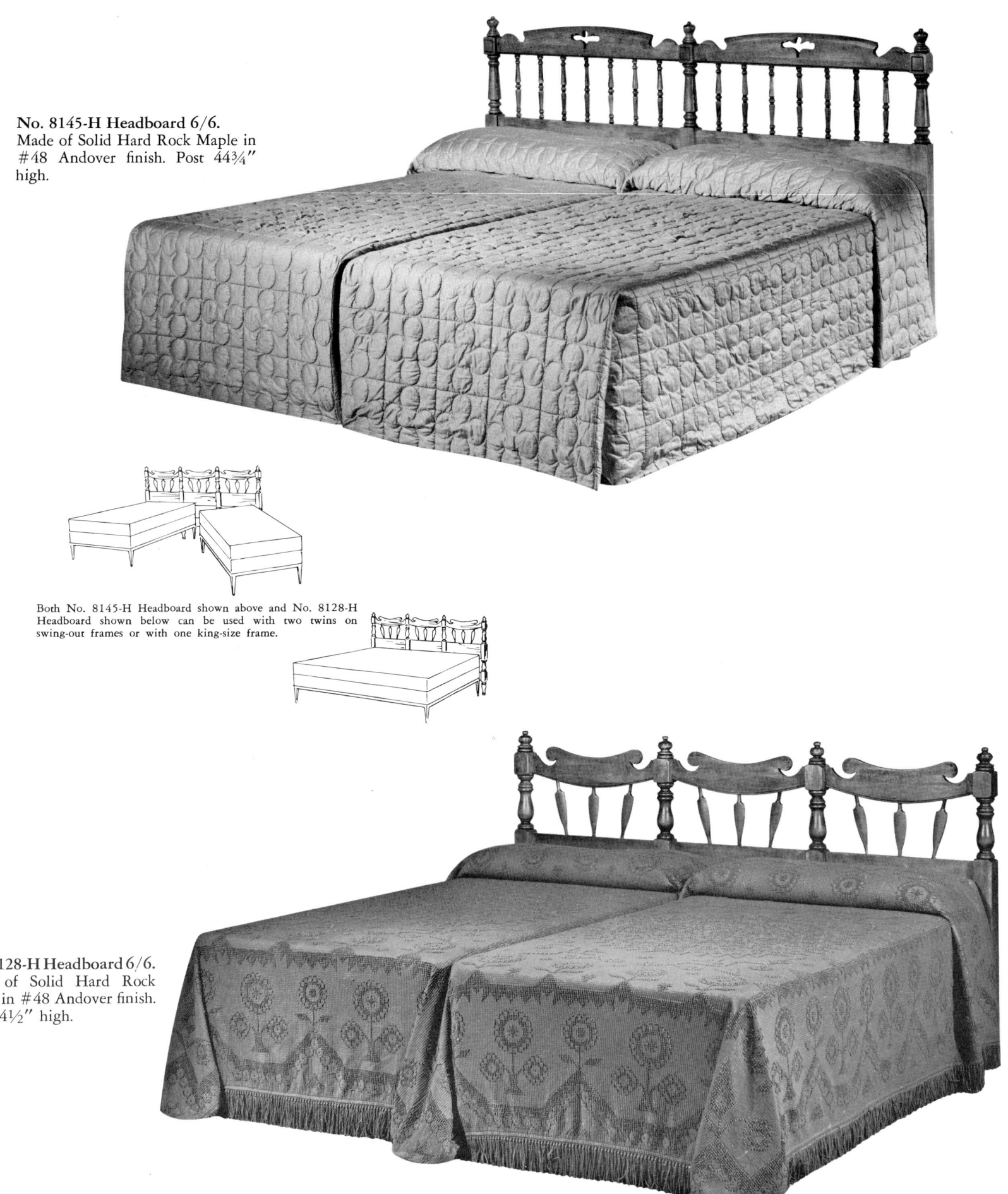

No. 8145-H Headboard 6/6.
Made of Solid Hard Rock Maple in #48 Andover finish. Post 44¾" high.

Both No. 8145-H Headboard shown above and No. 8128-H Headboard shown below can be used with two twins on swing-out frames or with one king-size frame.

No. 8128-H Headboard 6/6.
Made of Solid Hard Rock Maple in #48 Andover finish. Post 44½" high.

SOLID TABLES
with a Substantial Look

In keeping with the current "massive" look of provincial styling, these tables feature an unusual top with contoured corners, interestingly patterned door fronts and beautifully turned, substantial legs.

No. 8461 Lamp Table. Made of Solid Hard Rock Maple in #48 Andover finish. Top: 23" x 23". Height 20".

No. 8460 End Table. Made of Solid Hard Rock Maple in #48 Andover finish: Top 20" x 26". Height 20".

No one likes to be seated without a nearby table service on which to place a cup or deposit a hot cigarette ash which is rapidly approaching the fingers. Plan small tables convenient to seating pieces.

No. 8462 Ballustrade Cocktail Table. Made of Solid Hard Rock Maple in #48 Andover finish. Top 48" x 19". Height 15".

Tables with Hard Rock Maple Tops

No. 8422 Cocktail Table.
Made of Solid Hard Rock Maple in #48 Andover finish. Top. 52" x 20". Height 17".

No. 8421 Lamp Table.
Made of Solid Hard Rock Maple in #48 Andover finish. Top: 20" x 23". Height 24".

No. 8420 End Table.
Made of Solid Hard Rock Maple in #48 Andover finish. Top: 28" x 19". Height 22".

No. 8423 Cocktail Table.
Made of Solid Hard Rock Maple in #48 Andover finish. Top 46" x 19". Height 15".

A marproof, stain-resistant Formica table is the ideal setting for this cookies-and-hot-chocolate party! Recent improvements have given this finish a texture and soft luster that make it a perfect match for the solid maple of the base. As a result, more and more families with children choose this surface for their Early American tables.

There's a comfortable upholstered rocker near the fire for Mother, with a miniature decorated Boston Rocker for her daughter alongside. The cocktail table has its leaves up to double as a snack table and the maple footstools make excellent seats for small fry.

Near the window is a comfortable sofa flanked by two lamp tables of different styling. The fabric in the platform rocker is in gold to contrast with the warm burgundy of the sofa. Shutters painted to match the window frames make an unobtrusive backdrop for the grouping.

The area carpet extends just to the wood flooring of the entryway and a hall commode and mirror make a nice transition from the hall. In the hallway stands a decorated Deacon's Bench with a wall planter clock and hanging hatrack to welcome guests.

Coffee for the adults is being served on a unique table with a genuine porcelain platter top. The ladderback arm chair provides additional seating and may be moved into the dining room for extra guests.

All in all, this room is typical Early American — warm, casual and made for family living.

No. F-8412 Cocktail Table. Made of Solid Hard Rock Maple in #48 Andover finish. FORMICA top, maple grain. Leaves down 42" x 18". With leaves up 42" x 32". Height 15".

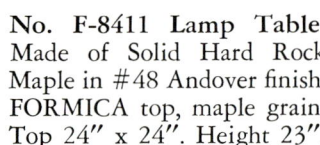

No. F-8411 Lamp Table. Made of Solid Hard Rock Maple in #48 Andover finish. FORMICA top, maple grain. Top 24" x 24". Height 23".

No. F-8410 End Table. Made of Solid Hard Rock Maple in #48 Andover finish. FORMICA top, maple grain. W 28" D 19" H 22¼".

No. F-821 Table. Made of Solid Hard Rock Maple in #48 Andover finish. With FORMICA top, maple grain. Legs pull out to support drop leaves. With leaves down 34" x 16". With leaves up 34" x 34". Height 28½".

tops surfaced with

Formica BRAND

laminated plastic

tops surfaced with FORMICA® BRAND laminated plastic

What could be more practical for tables that get hard day-to-day usage than tops surfaced with Formica brand laminated plastic? Formica is practically indestructible, resisting cigarette burns, food and drink stains. The grain pattern looks and feels so natural you can hardly tell it from the Solid Hard Rock Maple bases.

No. F-3177 Chairside Table. Made of Solid Hard Rock Maple in #48 Andover finish. FORMICA top surfaces. Brass ring for lifting. Each top surface 7¾" diameter. Over-all: 15" x 15". Height 19¼".

No. F-8436 End Table. Made of Solid Hard Rock Maple in #48 Andover finish. FORMICA top, Maple grain. Top: 28" x 21". Height 21½".

No. F-8437 Lamp Table. Made of Solid Hard Rock Maple in #48 Andover finish. FORMICA top, Maple grain. Top: 21" x 24". Height 21½".

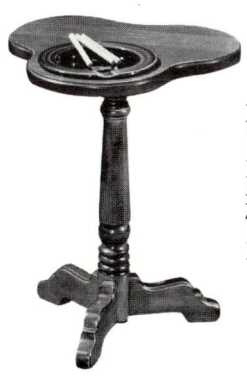

No. F-8444 Cigarette Table. Made of Solid Hard Rock Maple in #48 Andover finish. With FORMICA top. Top 14¼", Height 17½". Handmade ceramic ash tray.

No. F-8438 Cocktail Table. Made of Solid Hard Rock Maple in #48 Andover finish. FORMICA top, Maple grain. Top: 48" x 20". Height 15½".

Tables like these make interesting Accent Pieces

No. 8414 End Table. Made of Solid Hard Rock Maple in #48 Andover finish. Top: 20¼" x 28". Height 20".

No. D-847 Decorated Dough Box. Made of Solid Hard Rock Maple. Decorated in #75 Black and Gold or #74 Andover and Gold. Top: 28" x 18". Height 24".

No. 8415 Lamp Table. Made of Solid Hard Rock Maple in #48 Andover finish. Top: 23" x 23". Height 20".

No. 847 Dough Box. Made of Solid Hard Rock Maple in #48 Andover finish. Top: 28" x 18". Height 24".

No. 8416 Cocktail Table. Made of Solid Hard Rock Maple in #48 Andover finish. Top 46" x 18". With drop leaves up 46" x 30". Height 15¾".

Accent pieces add spice to your home!

Each room in your home can develop a distinct character of its own with the proper use of "accent pieces."

These focal points can be such items as hall commodes and mirrors illustrated or one of these attractive and useful storage cabinets.

No. 828 Dry Sink. Made of Solid Hard Rock Maple in #48 Andover finish. Copper Tray. FORMICA Serving Top. W 38″ D 18″ H 33″.

No. 844 Magazine Rack. Made of Solid Hard Rock Maple in #48 Andover finish. W 20″ D 16″ H 18″.

No. 826 Hall Commode. With 1 drawer. Made of Solid Hard Rock Maple in #48 Andover finish. W 32″ D 12″ H 31″.

No. 827 Hall Mirror. With Solid Cast Brass Eagle. Plate: 30″ x 18″. Over-all: 40″ x 22¾″.

No. D-826/D-827 in #74 Andover and Gold.

No. 894 Hall Commode. With one fixed shelf. Made of Solid Hard Rock Maple in #48 Andover finish. W 30″ D 12″ H 28¼″.

No. 895 Hall Mirror. Plate: 32″ x 16″. Over-all: 40¾″ x 19″. Solid Hard Rock Maple frame, #48 Andover finish.

No. 3163 Magazine Rack. Made of Solid Hard Rock Maple in #48 Andover finish. W 20″ D 12¼″ H 17″.

No. 8370 Cabinet. Made of Solid Hard Rock Maple in #48 Andover finish. W 48″ D 16″ H 27″.

No. 826/879 Curio Cabinet. Top has adjustable plate glass shelves. Illuminated with interior light #20. One drawer in base. Made of Solid Hard Rock Maple in #48 Andover finish. W 32″ D 12″ H 70½″.

No. 878/879 Plantation Desk. Top has adjustable plate glass shelves. Illuminated with interior light #20. One drawer in base. Made of Solid Hard Rock Maple in #48 Andover finish. W 32½″ D 18″ H 69¼″.

No. 877 Roll-Top Desk. Made of Solid Hard Rock Maple in #48 Andover finish. With 3 drawers. W 32″ D 18″ H 43″.

A desk is welcome in any room of the house, and like a toothbrush should not be considered community property. A HIS, a HERS, and as soon as the children are familiar with the word "homework," one for each of them.

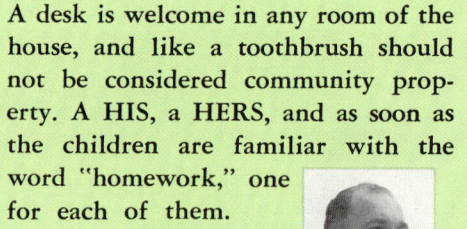

No. 3176 Fancy Mirror. Veneered frame trimmed in Black, Bird's-Eye Maple face. Plate 20″ x 38″. Over-all: W 22½″ D 1″ H 41½″.

No. 878 Writing Table. With 1 drawer. Made of Solid Hard Rock Maple in #48 Andover finish. W 32½″ D 18″ H 29¾″.

No. 875 Kneehole Desk. Made of Solid Hard Rock Maple in #48 Andover finish. With 7 drawers. W 50″ D 24″ H 30″.

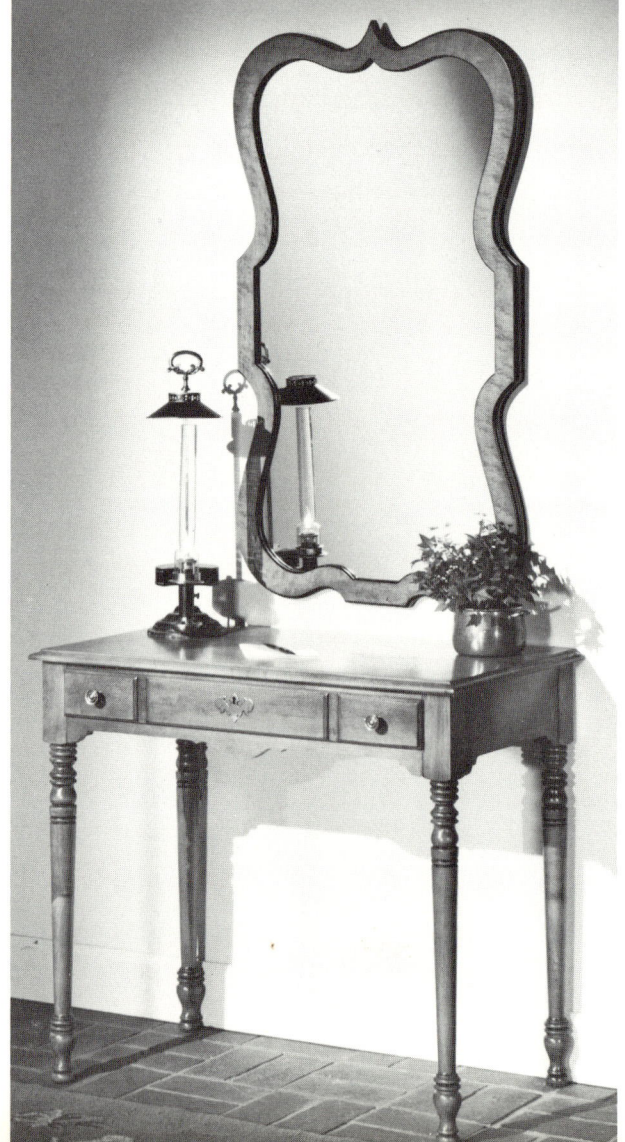

This family room features the No. 8370/8372 China with Crown Glass. In foreground is No. F-8163 Table and No. 8230 Rocker. In background is No. 8234 Upholstered Chair, No. 8233 Sofa, No. 8450 End Table and No. 8452 Cocktail Table. Accessories include No. 3136 Wood Shovel.

The warmth and cheeriness of Early American styling complement beauty and practicality in this family room. Beauty is achieved with such touches as the Crown Glass China, tangerine accent rug and print and solid colored upholstered pieces. The simulated brick vinyl floor, Formica top table and hooded fireplace are all very practical in a room designed for heavy family use. Simulated wood beams conceal lights which add a soft glow to the painted wood paneling and afford display for pewter pieces. Note the effective use of prints and plaques over the sofa.

YOUNG REPUBLIC GROUP
SOLID HARD ROCK MAPLE

No. 8254 Chair-and-a-Half. Made of Solid Hard Rock Maple in #48 Andover finish. Cushions are filled with equal parts Shredded Foam Rubber and Polyether Foam. Rubber webbing seat base. Seat: 29" wide, 20¼" deep. Over-all: W 39¼" D 30¾" H 35¾".

No. 8244 Upholstered Chair. Made of Solid Hard Rock Maple in #48 Andover finish. Cushions are filled with equal parts Shredded Foam Rubber and Polyether Foam. Rubber webbing seat base. Seat: 22" wide, 21½" deep. Over-all: W 29½" D 33½" H 38".

No. 8246 Upholstered Sofa. Made of Solid Hard Rock Maple in #48 Andover finish. Cushions are filled with equal parts Shredded Foam Rubber and Polyether Foam. Rubber webbing seat base. Seat: 64" wide, 21½" deep. Over-all: W 72" D 33½" H 38".

No. 8251 Chair. Made of Solid Hard Rock Maple in #48 Andover finish. Cushions are filled with equal parts Shredded Foam Rubber and Polyether Foam. Rubber webbing seat base. Seat: 23" wide, 20¼" deep. Over-all: W 33¾" D 30¾" H 35¾".

No. 8250 Rocker. Made of Solid Hard Rock Maple in #48 Andover finish. Cushions are filled with equal parts Shredded Foam Rubber and Polyether Foam. Rubber webbing seat base. Seat: 23" wide, 20¼" deep. Over-all: W 33¾" D 30¾" H 35".

No. 8253 Sofa. Made of Solid Hard Rock Maple in #48 Andover finish. Cushions are filled with equal parts Shredded Foam Rubber and Polyether Foam. Rubber webbing seat base. Seat: 63½" wide, 20¼" deep. Over-all: W 73" D 30¾" H 35¾".

No. 8252 Rocking Love Seat. Made of Solid Hard Rock Maple in #48 Andover finish. Cushions are filled with equal parts Shredded Foam Rubber and Polyether Foam. Rubber webbing seat base. Seat: 44" wide, 20¼" deep. Over-all: W 52½" D 30¾" H 35".

No. 8201 Wing Chair. Made of Solid Hard Rock Maple in #48 Andover finish. Cushions are filled with equal parts of Shredded Foam Rubber and Polyether Foam. Flat helical spring base. Seat: 22¼" wide, 20" deep. Over-all: W 30" D 29½" H 34".

No. 8203 Sofa. Made of Solid Hard Rock Maple in #48 Andover finish. Cushions are filled with equal parts Shredded Foam Rubber and Polyether Foam. Flat helical spring base. Seat: 60" wide, 20" deep. Over-all: W 67" D 29¾" H 34".

No. 8200 Wing Rocker. Made of Solid Rock Maple in #48 Andover finish. Cushions are filled with equal parts Shredded Foam Rubber and Polyether Foam. Flat helical spring base. Seat: 22¼" wide, 20" deep. Over-all: W 30" D 28½" H 33¼".

No. 8202 Rocking Love Seat. Made of Solid Hard Rock Maple in #48 Andover finish. Cushions filled with equal parts Shredded Foam Rubber and Polyether Foam. Flat helical spring base. Seat: 41¾" wide, 20" deep. Over-all: W 50¼" D 29½" H 34". Base equipped with block for locking in stationary position.

No. 8240 Ottoman. Made of Solid Hard Rock Maple in #48 Andover finish. Cushioning is equal parts Shredded Foam Rubber and Polyether Foam. Solid wood seat. Removable skirt. W 22″ D 15″ H 17½″.

No. 8232 Rocking Love Seat. Made of Solid Hard Rock Maple in #48 Andover finish. Seat is filled with equal parts Shredded Foam Rubber and Polyether Foam. Cotton back cushioning. Rubber webbing seat base. Seat: 42″ wide, 21″ deep. Over-all: W 43¾″ D 30″ H 38″. Base equipped with block for locking in stationary position.

No. 8230 Rocker. Made of Solid Hard Rock Maple in #48 Andover finish. Seat is filled with equal parts Shredded Foam Rubber and Polyether Foam. Cotton back cushioning. Rubber webbing seat base. Seat: 23″ wide, 21″ deep. Over-all: W 24½″ D 30″ H 38″.

No. 8233 Sofa. Made of Solid Hard Rock Maple in #48 Andover finish. Seat is filled with equal parts Shredded Foam Rubber and Polyether Foam. Cotton back cushioning. Rubber webbing seat base. Seat: 60½″ wide, 21″ deep. Over-all: W 64″ D 30″ H 38″.

No. 699 Upholstered Boston Rocker. Made of Selected Hardwoods in #48 Andover Maple finish. Seat is filled with equal parts Shredded Foam Rubber and Polyether Foam. Cotton back cushioning. Flat helical spring seat base. Seat: 22″ wide, 19″ deep. Over-all: W 26½″ D 35¼″ H 42½″.

No. D-699 Decorated in #75 Black and Gold.

No. W-699 Decorated in #72 White and Gold.

No. 8225 Wing Back Rocker. Made of Solid Hard Rock Maple in #48 Andover finish. Seat base is rubber webbing. Seat cushion is filled with equal parts Shredded Foam Rubber and Polyether Foam. Cotton back cushioning. Seat: 23″ wide, 18½″ deep. Over-all: W 28″ D 28¾″ H 36¼″.

No. W-698 Cushioned Boston Rocker. Made of Selected Hardwoods. Decorated in #72 White and Gold. Seat is filled with equal parts Shredded Foam Rubber and Polyether Foam. Cotton back cushioning. Solid wood seat. Seat: 21½″ wide, 20″ deep. Over-all: W 26″ D 34½″ H 40½″.

No. D-698 Cushioned Boston Rocker decorated in #75 Black and Gold.

No. A-698 in #86 Antique Blue, #87 Antique Green, #88 Antique Red or #89 Antique Yellow finish.

No. 698 Cushioned Boston Rocker in #48 Andover Maple finish.

No. 8240 Ottoman. Made of Solid Hard Rock Maple in #48 Andover finish. Cushioning is equal parts Shredded Foam Rubber and Polyether Foam. Solid wood seat. Removable skirt. W 22″ D 15″ H 17½″.

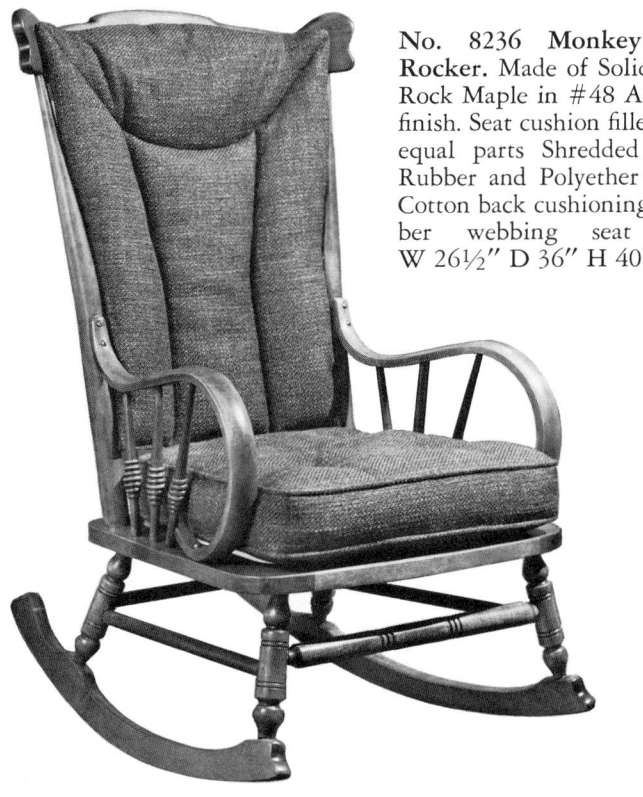

No. 8236 Monkey Tail Rocker. Made of Solid Hard Rock Maple in #48 Andover finish. Seat cushion filled with equal parts Shredded Foam Rubber and Polyether Foam. Cotton back cushioning. Rubber webbing seat base. W 26½″ D 36″ H 40½″.

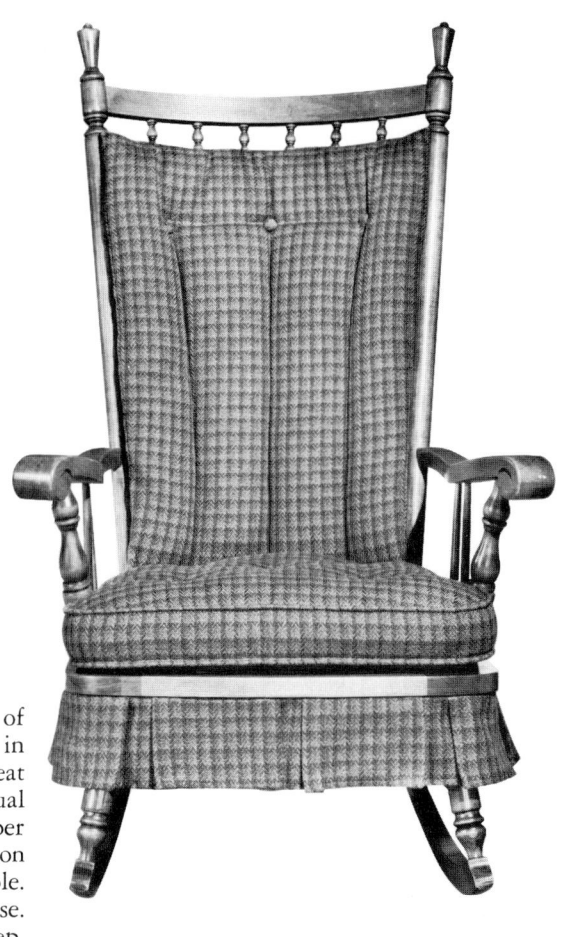

No. 8218 Big Boy. Made of Solid Hard Rock Maple in #48 Andover finish. Seat cushion filled with equal parts Shredded Foam Rubber and Polyether Foam. Cotton back cushion is reversible. Rubber webbing seat base. Seat: 22″ wide, 19½″ deep. Over-all: W 28″ D 35½″ H 46½″.

No. 8256 Cushioned Rocker. Made of Solid Hard Rock Maple in #48 Andover Maple finish. Seat is filled with equal parts Shredded Foam Rubber and Polyether Foam. Cotton back cushioning. Solid wood seat. Seat: 22″ wide, 19″ deep. Over-all: W 25¾″ D 33½″ H 43½″.

No. 8214 Cottage Rocker. Made of Solid Hard Rock Maple in #48 Andover finish. Seat cushion filled with equal parts Shredded Foam Rubber and Polyether Foam. Cotton back cushion is reversible. Solid wood seat. Seat: 20½″ wide, 18″ deep. Over-all: W 26″ D 32″ H 38″.

No. 8242 Stub Chair. Made of Solid Hard Rock Maple in #48 Andover finish. Foam Rubber seat cushions. Rubber webbing seat base. Seat: 20½" wide, 17½" deep. Over-all: W 25½" D 25¾" H 27¾".

No. 8234 Upholstered Chair. Made of Solid Hard Rock Maple in #48 Andover finish. Seat is filled with equal parts Shredded Foam Rubber and Polyether Foam. Cotton back cushioning. Rubber webbing seat base. Seat: 22" wide, 19¼" deep. Over-all: W 29" D 32¼" H 45¾".

No. 8208 Swivel Rocker. Made of Solid Hard Rock Maple in #48 Andover finish. Seat is filled with equal parts Shredded Foam Rubber and Polyether Foam. Cotton back cushioning. Rubber webbing seat base. Seat: 22¾" wide, 20" deep. Over-all: W 30" D 20" H 41".

No. 8209 Swivel Rocker. Made of Solid Hard Rock Maple in #48 Andover finish. Seat is filled with equal parts Shredded Foam Rubber and Polyether Foam. Cotton back cushioning. Rubber webbing seat base. Seat: 21½" wide, 20" deep. Over-all: W 25½" D 30" H 44".

Color, color . . . and more color is the great trend in decorating today! Bold hues are this season's motif in carpeting, wall coverings, draperies, cover materials—and furniture.

For this reason, many of our most popular, time-tested rocker patterns are being made available in solid colors and color combinations.

The rockers illustrated above feature hand-glazed antique finishes in blue, green, red or yellow, that provide a refreshing contrast to their natural-hued companions. These finishes are authentic Early American tones and the hand glazing gives a distinctive finishing touch that delights the color-conscious homemaker.

An interesting contrast is provided on some patterns, as shown on pages 68 and 69, by finishing the wood seat in natural maple and the remainder of the rocker in either white and gold or black and gold.

For still greater color impact, some of the upholstered models with their gay prints may be obtained in blue, green, red or yellow finishes.

Descriptive Information:

No. A-660 Boston Rocker	Page 69
No. A-698 Boston Rocker	Page 64
No. A-684 Farmhouse Rocker	Page 71

YOUNG REPUBLIC GROUP
SOLID HARD ROCK MAPLE

BOSTON ROCKERS
are favorites for all

A curious thing about the Boston Rocker is that almost everybody knows what it is and almost nobody knows anything about where or when it developed. The Boston Rocker probably did not even originate in Boston. Certainly it was made in many regions beginning in the 1830's. Tell City has been making Boston Rockers for generations and they were never more popular than they are today.

No. D-646 Boston Rocker. Made of Selected Hardwoods in #75 Black and Gold. Seat: 19¾" wide, 16¼" deep. Over-all: W 23¾" D 29¼" H 41½".

No. W-646 Decorated in #72 White and Gold.

No. 646 Boston Rocker. Made of Selected Hardwoods in choice of #27 Mahogany finish or #48 Andover Maple finish. Seat: 19¾" wide, 16¼" deep. Over-all: W 23¾" D 29¼" H 41½".

No. B-660 Boston Rocker. Made of Selected Hardwoods. Decorated in #55 Black and Gold with Andover Maple finish seat. Shaped back. Seat: 20" wide, 17¾" deep. Over-all: W 23¾" D 28½" H 41¾".

No. W-650 Boston Rocker. Made of Selected Hardwoods. Decorated in #72 White and Gold. Seat: 20" wide, 17¾" deep. Over-all: W 24" D 29" H 42¼".

No. D-650 Boston Rocker. Decorated in #75 Black and Gold and #74 Andover and Gold. See color illustration on page 72.

No. 650 Boston Rocker. Made of Selected Hardwoods in choice of #27 Mahogany finish, #30 Walnut finish, #48 Andover Maple finish or #95 Cherry finish. Seat: 20" wide, 17¾" deep. Over-all: W 24" D 29" H 42¼".

No. E-660 Boston Rocker. Made of Selected Hardwoods. Decorated in #52 White and Gold with Andover Maple finish seat. Shaped back. Seat: 20" wide, 17¾" deep. Over-all: W 23¾" D 28½" H 41¾".

No. D-660 Boston Rocker. Made of Selected Hardwoods. Decorated in #75 Black and Gold or #74 Andover and Gold. Shaped back. Seat: 20" wide, 17¾" deep. Over-all: W 23¾" D 28½" H 41¾".

No. W-660 Decorated in #72 White and Gold.

No. 660 Boston Rocker. Made of Selected Hardwoods in #27 Mahogany finish, #30 Walnut finish, #48 Andover Maple finish or #95 Cherry finish. Shaped back. Seat: 20" wide, 17¾" deep. Over-all: W 23¾" D 28½" H 41¾".

No. A-660 Boston Rocker in #86 Antique Blue finish, #87 Antique Green finish, #88 Antique Red finish or #89 Antique Yellow finish.

No. D-677 Boston Rocker. Made of Selected Hardwoods. Decorated in #75 Black and Gold. Shaped back. Seat: 20¾" wide, 17½" deep. Over-all: W 23½" D 28¼" H 42¼".

No. W-677 Boston Rocker. Made of Selected Hardwoods. Decorated in #72 White and Gold. Shaped back. Seat: 20¾" wide, 17½" deep. Over-all: W 23½" D 28¼" H 42¼".

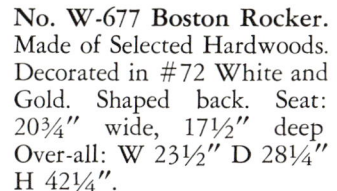

No. 677 Boston Rocker. Made of Selected Hardwoods in choice of #27 Mahogany finish, #30 Walnut finish, #48 Andover Maple finish or #95 Cherry finish. Shaped back. Seat: 20¾" wide, 17½" deep. Over-all: W 23½" D 28¼" H 42¼".

CHILDREN'S ROCKERS

No. 25 Child's Windsor Rocker. Made of Selected Hardwoods in choice of #27 Mahogany finish or #48 Andover Maple finish. Seat: 16" wide, 12¼" deep. Over-all: W 21" D 24½" H 26¾".

No. 29 Child's Boston Rocker. Made of Selected Hardwoods in choice of #27 Mahogany finish or #48 Andover Maple finish. Seat: 15¼" wide, 12¾" deep. Over-all: W 17" W 21¼" H 27½".

Companion to No. 650 shown on Page 68.

No. W-29 Child's Boston Rocker. Made of Selected Hardwoods. Decorated in #72 White and Gold. Seat: 15¼" wide, 12¾" deep. Over-all: W 17" D 21¼" H 27½".

Companion to No. W-650 shown on Page 68.

No. D-29 Child's Boston Rocker. Made of Selected Hardwoods. Decorated in #75 Black and Gold. Seat: 15¼" wide, 12¾" deep. Over-all: W 17" D 21¼" H 27½".

Companion to No. D-650 shown on Page 68.

One of the most functional and welcoming features of a kitchen is a rocking chair. This farm house rocker is equally at home as shown before a real New England fireplace formerly used for cooking, as in a modern setting complete with every labor-saving device known to man. No woman is ever too sophisticated to interrupt a culinary stint with the welcome rhythm of a rocker. Here we see a corner of a kitchen done in quiet warm beige and avocado. White Formica counter tops provide a clean, sharp accent to the otherwise mellow surroundings.

No. 684 Farm House Rocker. Made of Selected Hardwoods in choice of #30 Walnut finish, #48 Andover Maple finish or #95 Cherry finish. Seat: 20¾" wide, 16½" deep. Over-all: W 24¼" D 29¼" H 37½".

No. A-684 Farm House Rocker. In #86 Antique Blue finish, #87 Antique Green finish, #88 Antique Red finish or #89 Antique Yellow finish.

No. D-684 Farm House Rocker. Made of Selected Hardwoods. Decorated in #75 Black and Gold or #74 Andover and Gold: Seat: 20¾" wide, 16½" deep. Over-all: W 24¼" D 29¼" H 37½".

Illustrated is No. D-650 Boston Rocker.

> **No. 600**
> *Tie-on Cushion Set*
> **FOR BOSTON ROCKERS**

Cushions for rockers 646, 650, 660 and 677 may be purchased separately as No. 600 Cushion Set which fits all.

Cushions are filled with equal parts of Shredded Foam Rubber and Polyether Foam.

Patterns illustrated below and designated by the letter "C" include both Rocker and Tie-on Cushion Set.

No. 646-C Cushioned Boston Rocker. Made of Selected Hardwoods in choice of #27 Mahogany finish or #48 Andover Maple finish. Shaped back. Seat: 19¾" wide, 16¼" deep. Over-all: W 23¾" D 29¼" H 41½".

No. D-646-C Decorated in #75 Black and Gold.

No. W-646-C Decorated in #72 White and Gold.

No. 677-C Cushioned Boston Rocker. Made of Selected Hardwoods in #27 Mahogany finish, #30 Walnut finish, #48 Andover Maple finish or #95 Cherry finish. Shaped back. Seat: 20¾" wide, 17½" deep. Over-all: W 23½" D 28¼" H 42¼".

No. D-677-C Decorated in #75 Black and Gold.

No. W-677-C Decorated in #72 White and Gold.

No. 650-C Cushioned Boston Rocker. Made of Selected Hardwoods in #27 Mahogany finish, #30 Walnut finish, #48 Andover Maple finish or #95 Cherry finish. Shaped back. Seat: 20" wide, 17¾" deep. Over-all: W 24" D 29" H 42¼".

No. D-650-C Decorated in #74 Andover and Gold or #75 Black and Gold.

No. W-650-C Decorated in #72 White and Gold.

No. 660-C Cushioned Boston Rocker. Made of Selected Hardwoods in #27 Mahogany finish, #30 Walnut finish, #48 Andover Maple finish or #95 Cherry finish. Shaped back. Seat: 20" wide, 17¾" deep. Over-all: W 23¾" D 28½" H 41¾".

No. D-660-C Decorated in #75 Black and Gold or #74 Andover and Gold.

No. W-660-C Decorated in #72 White and Gold.

No. A-660-C in #86 Antique Blue, #87 Antique Green, #88 Antique Red, or #89 Antique Yellow finish.

No. W-2400 Settle. Made of Selected Hardwoods. Decorated in #72 White and Gold. Seat: 36" wide, 16½" deep. Over-all: W 36½" D 21" H 34½".

No. D-2400 Settle in #75 Black and Gold.

No. 8400 Settle. Made of Solid Hard Rock Maple in #48 Andover finish. Seat: 36" wide, 16½" deep. Over-all: W 36½" D 21" H 34½".

No. 8404 Deacon's Bench. Made of Solid Hard Rock Maple in #48 Andover finish. Seat: 60" wide, 15½" deep. Over-all: W 62" D 21" H 34".

No. 8023 Telephone Bench. Made of Solid Hard Rock Maple in #48 Andover finish. Choice of fabrics for Cotton slip seat. Seat: 28" wide, 15¼" deep. Over-all: W 32" D 20" H 28½".

No. D-2404 Deacon's Bench. Made of Solid Hard Rock Maple. Decorated in #75 Black and Gold. Seat: 60" wide, 15½" deep. Over-all: W 62" D 21" H 34".

Swivel Stools
FOR BAR OR KITCHEN

Tell City offers these attractive swivel stools in three sizes. A choice of 30", 24" and 17" seat heights assures you the right stool for your home. Footrest rings are brass-plated steel.

No. 2219 Swivel Chair. Made of Solid Hard Rock Maple in #48 Andover finish. Seat: 14½" wide, 13½" deep. Seat Height: 17". Over-all: W 20" D 20" H 29½".

No. 2217 Swivel Stool. Made of Solid Hard Rock Maple in #48 Andover finish. Seat: 14½" wide, 13½" deep. Seat Height: 24". Over-all W 20" D 20" H 36½".

No. 2218 Swivel Stool. Made of Solid Hard Rock Maple in #48 Andover finish. Seat: 14½" wide, 13½" deep. Seat Height: 30". Over-all: W 20" D 20" H 42½".

DECORATOR CHAIRS...

Today's trend toward more dramatic ornamental accents in "conversation piece" furnishings can be brilliantly (and economically!) fulfilled with the addition of these beautiful, decorative chairs, in sets to flavor conventional dining groups, or as focal pieces in living rooms, bedrooms, and foyers. Ideal for desk, piano, or dressing table.

Seat Fabric: Both 6300 and 6304 available in your choice of O-604 Red Velvet or I-69 Gold Matelassé.

No. D-6300 Spindle Back Chair
Made of Selected Hardwoods
Decorated in #75 Black and Gold
Seat: 17" wide, 15¾" deep
Over-all: W 17" D 18¾" H 35½"

No. W-6300 in #72 White and Gold

No. 6300 in #77 Gilt finish

No. D-6304 Spool Back Chair
Made of Selected Hardwoods
Decorated in #75 Black and Gold
Seat: 16¼" wide, 15¾" deep
Over-all: W 16¼" D 17¾" H 32¾"

No. W-6304 in #72 White and Gold

No. 6304 in #77 Gilt finish

No. 8405 Milking Stool
#48 Andover finish
W 16" L 15" H 12½"

Decorative and Comfortable Footstools

The No. 8405 Milking Stool is made of Solid Hard Rock Maple in #48 Andover finish. Other stools are made of Selected Hardwoods, in choice of #48 Andover Maple finish and #95 Cherry finish. The No. 2230 Needlepoint Footstool is available only in the light cover #751 or the Black cover #750. All other stools available in any cover illustrated except the two needlepoint covers #750 and #751.

No. 2230
Needlepoint Footstool
Cover: 750
#48 Andover Maple finish
(at left)
Cover: 751
#95 Cherry finish
(at right)
W 8" L 10½" H 6¾"

No. 2231
Oval Footstool
#48 Andover Maple finish
Cover: F-153
(at left)
Cover: 752
#95 Cherry finish
(at right)
W 10" L 14" H 6¼"

No. 2234
Footstool
Cover: F-167
#48 Andover Maple finish
(at left)
Cover: F-162
#95 Cherry finish
(at right)
W 10" L 19" H 10"

A footstool provides a nice accent when covered with needlepoint or a colorful Early American pattern.

Tell City Lamps and Decorative Accessories are a treasure trove of Early Americana. They are the result of two years of research in museums, in private collections, and in libraries and represent the cream of hundreds of ideas based on authentic antique patterns. Each is carefully crafted in the 102-year-old Tell City tradition and bears the mark of much skilled handwork. You will display these proudly in your home and enjoy them every day of your life because they carry so beautifully the nostalgic echoes of a cherished bygone era.

Lamps and Decorative Accessories

No. 3167 Button Box
Smart little sewing box with spool holders, pincushion and drawer for scissors and buttons. Made of Solid Hard Rock Maple in #48 Andover finish. W 9¾" D 6¼" H 4½".

No. 3146 Treasure Chest. A sturdy chest designed for holding treasured trinkets and keepsakes. Made of Solid Hard Rock Maple in #48 Andover finish. H 5½" W 13" D 9½".

No. A-3146 Treasure Chest. Same as above except in #86 Antique Blue, #87 Antique Green, #88 Antique Red or #89 Antique Yellow finish.

No. 3112 Tambour Secretary
A miniature roll-top desk patterned from a very valuable antique. Holds stationery, pens and correspondence. Secret drawer for confidential records. H 9" W 11½" D 10½". Made of Solid Maple in #48 Andover finish.

No. 3101 Clamp Book Ends
Early furniture craftsmen used wooden clamps like these for cabinetmaking in Colonial days. H 8" W 2½". Made of Solid Hard Rock Maple in #48 Andover finish. Sold in pairs.

No. A-3180 Book Ends. These bookends look like they are cast, but are made of cleverly decorated wood. Page edges are glazed gold. Made of Solid Hard Rock Maple in #86 Antique Blue finish, #87 Antique Green finish, #88 Antique Red finish or #89 Antique Yellow finish. W 10¼" D 7" H 6¼". Sold in pairs.

No. 3182 Candlesticks. A handsomely turned pair of candlesticks that can be used effectively with any provincial style. Made of Solid Hard Rock Maple in #48 Andover finish. H 14" W 3½".

No. A-3182 Candlesticks. Finished in #86 Antique Blue, #87 Antique Green, #88 Antique Red or #89 Antique Yellow finish. Made of Solid Hard Rock Maple. Sold in pairs.

No. 3108 Candlestick
An Early American version of the large, heavy candlesticks so popular today. Can be used singly or in pairs. H 11¼" Diameter 5½". Made of Solid Hard Rock Maple in #48 Andover finish. Sold individually.

No. 3130 Coat Bar. This truly "different" coat bar has solid brass knobs and hooks. An extremely ornamental, yet useful piece! H 5″ W 45¼″ D 8¼″. Made of Solid Hard Rock Maple in #48 Andover finish.

No. 3115 Hat Tree. This authentic reproduction of a Georgian antique is functional and attractive. Hooks are solid cast brass. H 39″ W 14¾″ D 10¾″. Made of Solid Hard Rock Maple in #48 Andover finish.

No. 3150 Bentwood Coat Rack. Patterned after an antique rack with unusual turnings. Made of Solid Hard Rock Maple in #48 Andover finish. W 20½″ H 10½″ D 8½″.

No. 3126 Shelf Coat Rack
A utility piece that combines a wall shelf with a coat rack. Black hat pegs have turned brass tips. Hooks are solid cast brass. H 10½″ W 29¾″ D 7″. Made of Solid Hard Rock Maple in #48 Andover finish.

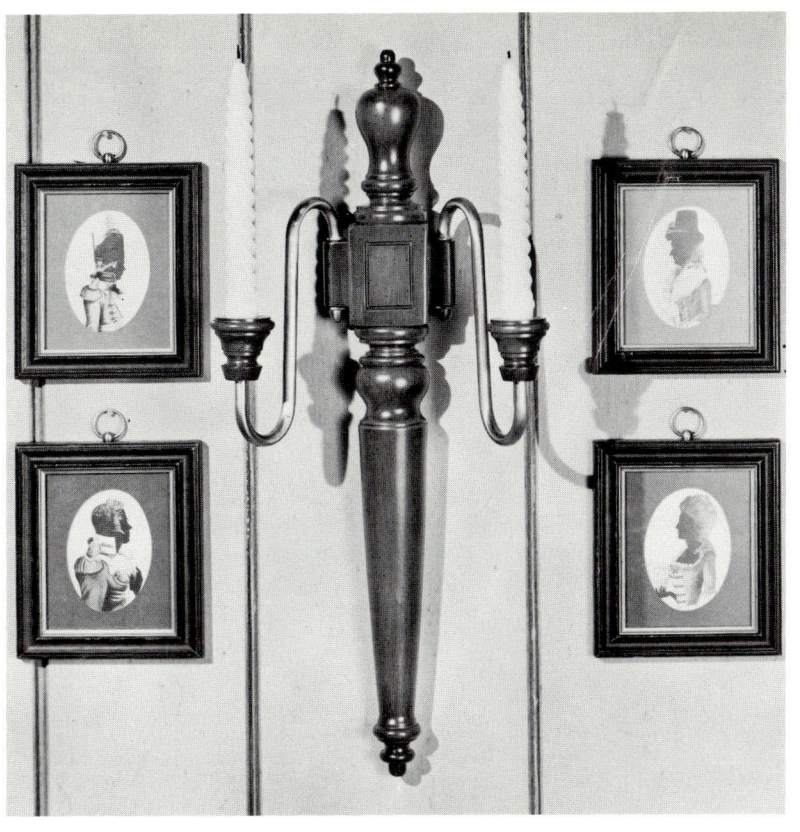
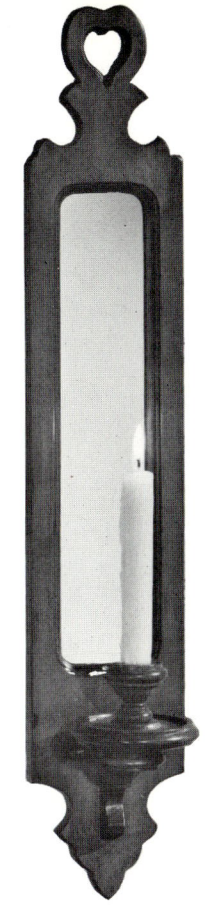
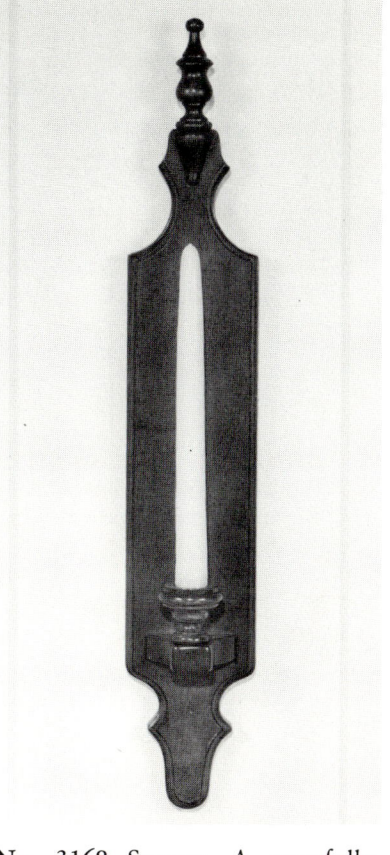

No. A-3186 Sconce. An extremely ornamental wall piece with an interesting turned stem and brass-plated candle arms. Suitable for any decor. Made of Solid Hard Rock Maple in #86 Antique Blue finish, #87 Antique Green finish, #88 Antique Red finish or #89 Antique Yellow finish. H 21½" W 12¼" D 4".

No. 3103 Mirrored Sconce Reflecting mirror enhances the candlelight. Turned candle holder adds richness to base. Use singly or in pairs. H 24¾" W 4½" D 4½". Made of Solid Hard Rock Maple in #48 Andover finish.

No. 3168 Sconce. A gracefully contoured wall piece made of Solid Hard Rock Maple in #48 Andover finish. W 3½" D 3¾" H 22¼".

No. A-3168 Sconce. Same as above but offered in choice of four Antique finishes including #86 Antique Blue finish, #87 Antique Green finish, #88 Antique Red finish and #89 Antique Yellow finish.

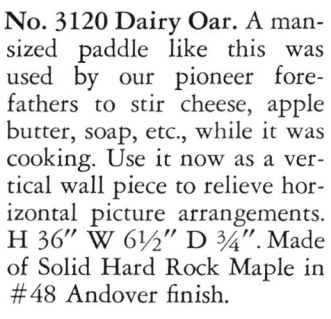

No. 3120 Dairy Oar. A man-sized paddle like this was used by our pioneer forefathers to stir cheese, apple butter, soap, etc., while it was cooking. Use it now as a vertical wall piece to relieve horizontal picture arrangements. H 36" W 6½" D ¾". Made of Solid Hard Rock Maple in #48 Andover finish.

No. 3136 Wood Shovel. An adaptation of one of the handmade wood shovels used widely in Early America. Heavy Solid Hard Rock Maple in #48 Andover finish. W 18¼" H 34½".

No. A-3183 Castle Key. A large wall piece with interesting design. Hangs vertically or horizontally. Made of Solid Hard Rock Maple in choice of four antique finishes: #86 Antique Blue finish, #87 Antique Green finish, #88 Antique Red finish or #89 Antique Yellow finish. 25¼" x 7".

No. 3131 Wastebasket. Just the sort of a solid wastebasket a man likes. Green interior with attractive brass studs on outside. Excellent decorator piece for magazines or artificial plants. H 15⅛". Diameter: 12⅜" top, 8½" bottom. Made of Solid Hard Rock Maple in #48 Andover finish.

No. A-3131 same as above except in #86 Antique Blue finish, #87 Antique Green finish, #88 Antique Red finish or #89 Antique Yellow finish.

No. 844 Magazine Rack. Made of Solid Hard Rock Maple in #48 Andover finish. W 20" D 16" H 18".

No. F-3177 Chairside Table. A small, move-about table for ash trays, drinks, etc. Has three separate Formica brand laminated plastic tops and a brass ring for lifting. Substantial pedestal base. Made of Solid Hard Rock Maple in #48 Andover finish. 15" x 15" diameter. 19¼" high. Individual tops 7¾" in diameter.

No. 3163 Magazine Rack. Made of Solid Hard Rock Maple in #48 Andover finish. W 20" D 12¼" H 17".

No. F-8444 Cigarette Table. Made of Solid Hard Rock Maple in #48 Andover finish. Has Formica brand laminated plastic top. Top 14¼", Height 17½". Handmade ceramic ash tray.

No. 3179 Magazine Bin. A hanging magazine rack that can be hung wherever magazines are read, including the bathroom. Roomy container with front supported by leather thongs. Made of Solid Hard Rock Maple in #48 Andover finish. W 18" D 18½" H 19½".

No. 3175 Birdcage Wastebasket. A most unusual wastebasket whose design is based upon the bird cages made in this fashion years ago. Liner is practical plastic, removable. Made of Solid Hard Rock Maple in #48 Andover finish. Top 13½" x 10½". 13½" high.

Accessories hanging on wall from left to right are: No. A-3144 Planter Clock, No. A-3165 Octagon Mirror, No. A-3168 Sconce, No. A-3134 Oval Mirror, No. A-3148 Looking Glass and No. A-3185 Eagle Mirror. Clocks on post from top down are No. 3178 Pendulum Clock and two No. A-3166 Wag Clocks. On floor are four No. A-3131 Wastebaskets, a No. A-3182 Candlestick and a No. A-3146 Treasure Chest. On the No. 8121 Table is No. 3327/5548 Turned Lamp.

The decorating-minded homemaker will often discover that one or more colored accessories provide the right accent that turns an ordinary setting into a charmingly different room.

Antique colors such as those illustrated above are based upon true Early American hues. Although these colors are bright, they have a hand-glazed surface which blends perfectly with the warm, mellow tones of maple.

Such accessories may be placed at strategic spots on the floor, hung from the wall or placed on tables or shelves.

For interesting effects the color of your accessories may be selected to blend with drapery, upholstery fabrics or floor coverings.

Here is your key to imaginative decorating with the touch of individuality that transforms *a* room into *your* room.

TELL CITY CHAIR COMPANY
TELL CITY, IND.

No. 3143 Wall Clock.
This clock is battery operated using an imported German movement. Brass dial with glazed white face. Will run one year on ordinary flashlight battery. W 12¾" H 29". Made of Solid Hard Rock Maple in #48 Andover finish.

No. A-3166 Wag Clock.
This clock goes beautifully with Early American as well as other styles. Has an imported German key-wind 8-day movement with brass pendulum. Made of Selected Hardwoods in choice of #86 Antique Blue finish, #87 Antique Green finish, #88 Antique Red finish or #89 Antique Yellow finish. W 14" D 3¼" H 22".

No. 3144 Planter Clock.
This clock is battery operated using an imported German movement. Early American styling with planter box for plastic ivy, etc. Will run one year on ordinary flashlight battery. W 11" D 3½" H 29¼". Made of Solid Hard Rock Maple in #48 Andover finish.

No. A-3144 Planter Clock.
Same as above except in choice of #86 Antique Blue finish, #87 Antique Green finish, #88 Antique Red finish or #89 Antique Yellow finish.

No. A-3184 Cottage Clock.
This versatile clock has a metal face with hinged glass and uses an imported battery movement. Offered in choice of four antique colors: #86 Antique Blue finish, #87 Antique Green finish, #88 Antique Red finish or #89 Antique Yellow finish. W 12¾" D 3" H 12¾".

No. 3178 Pendulum Clock. An attractively shaped clock with a handsomely styled maple frame and wag pendulum. Imported battery powered pendulum movement. Made of Solid Hard Rock Maple in #48 Andover finish. W 12" D 4¼" H 21¼".

No. 3124 Banjo Clock. A beautifully decorated clock with imported German movement. Will run for a year on one ordinary flashlight battery. Eliminates electric cords — can be mounted anywhere. H 36" W 10½" D 2¼". Made of Solid Hard Rock Maple in #48 Andover finish.

No. 3162 Lantern Clock. Inspired by the ever-popular coach lanterns. Imported German battery movement. Antiqued face and decorative black hands. Brass eagle finial on top. Made of Solid Hard Rock Maple in #48 Andover finish with green accents. W 8" D 3¾" H 32¾".

Nothing detracts from the beauty of a clock like an unsightly cord reaching down to an electrical outlet. All clocks on these pages are cordless with self-contained power units and can be placed anywhere.

No. 3116 Shelf Planter
A beautiful wall shelf as well as a useful planter. Note the intricate detailing of the spool railing and the fine sculpturing of the solid cast brass ringed lions. H 4″ W 28½″ D 6¾″. Made of Solid Hard Rock Maple in #48 Andover finish.

No. 3123 Corner Whatnot.
The unusual feature of this classic corner shelf piece is the hinged drawer which swings out for easy access. H 34″ W 12″ D 9″. Made of Solid Hard Rock Maple in #48 Andover finish.

No. 3171 Tier Shelf.
Vertical wall shelf or what-not with 3-tier shelves. Made of Solid Hard Rock Maple in #48 Andover finish. W 12″ D 5¼″ H 31¼″.

No. 3174 Acorn Bracket.
Just made for displaying that one prize piece of statuary or what have you. Can be used in pairs of several, for displaying a collection. With acorn teardrop motif. Made of Solid Hard Rock Maple in #48 Andover finish. W 10¼″ D 4¾″ H 5¾″.

No. 3159 Bracket Shelf.
Made of Solid Hard Rock Maple in #48 Andover finish. Features an unusual skirt with heart cutouts. W 22″ D 6″ H 7″.

No. 3181 Candlestick Shelf.
A truly Early American style adapted from an antique shelf. Can be used for a candle or to hold a figurine, a pot of ivy or other treasures. Made of Solid Hard Rock Maple in #48 Andover finish. W 6¾″ D 5″ H 17¾″.

No. A-3181 Candlestick Shelf.
Same as above in choice of four antique finishes. #86 Antique Blue finish, #87 Antique Green finish, #88 Antique Red finish or #89 Antique Yellow finish.

No. 3169 Shelf. An interesting and useful wall piece, with a gallery and teardrop design. Made of Solid Hard Rock Maple in #48 Andover finish. W 25″ D 7¼″ H 5½″.

No. 3158 Corner Shelf. A classic 3-shelf corner piece for knickknacks. Made of Solid Hard Rock Maple in #48 Andover finish. W 11¼″ D 8″ H 31¼″.

No. A-3185 Eagle Mirror.
A Solid Rock Maple frame with a crown in #48 Andover finish, and an eagle stenciled in Gold. Frame available in choice of four Antique finishes: #86 Antique Blue finish, #87 Antique Green finish, #88 Antique Red finish or #89 Antique Yellow finish. W 14¾" D 2½" H 20¼". Plate 12" x 12".

No. 3134 Oval Mirror.
An attractive size and shape that can be used with many wall groupings. W 14¾" H 18½". Made of Solid Hard Rock Maple in #48 Andover finish.

No. A-3134 Oval Mirror same as above except in choice of #86 Antique Blue finish, #87 Antique Green finish, #88 Antique Red finish or #89 Antique Yellow finish.

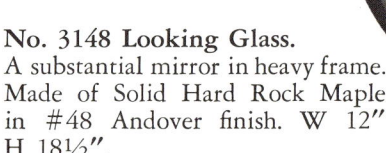

No. 3148 Looking Glass.
A substantial mirror in heavy frame. Made of Solid Hard Rock Maple in #48 Andover finish. W 12" H 18½".

No. A-3148 Looking Glass same as above except in choice of #86 Antique Blue finish, #87 Antique Green finish, #88 Antique Red finish or #89 Antique Yellow finish.

No. D-8309 Standing Swivel Decorated Mirror. Features hand-scooped trough in base. Made of Solid Hard Rock Maple. Decorated in #74 Andover and Gold finish. Over-all: 20" x 16½". Plate 14" x 10".

No. 8309 Standing Swivel Mirror in #48 Andover finish.

No. A-3165 Octagon Mirror.
Made of Solid Hard Rock Maple in #86 Antique Blue finish, #87 Antique Green finish, #88 Antique Red finish or #89 Antique Yellow finish. Plate 14¼" x 14¼". Frame 16½" x 16½".

No. 3165 Octagon Mirror same as above except in #48 Andover Maple finish.

No. 3172 Wall Console.
A hanging console that is especially useful in a hall. One drawer. Made of Solid Hard Rock Maple in #48 Andover finish. W 28" D 10¼" H 17¼". (Shown with No. 3173 Mirror described at right.)

No. 3173 Mirror.
Made of Solid Hard Rock Maple in #48 Andover finish. Plate 16" x 30". Over-all: W 18¾" D 2" H 38¼".

No. 3172 Wall Console
shown with
No. 3176 Fancy Mirror
described at left.

No. 3176 Fancy Mirror.
Veneered frame trimmed in black. Bird's-Eye Maple face. Plate 20" x 38". Over-all: W 22½" D 1" H 41½".

Lamps illustrated, from left to right are: No. A-3324/5542 Table Lamp, No. A-3321/5539 Table Lamp, No. A-3322/5540 Table Lamp, No. A-3329/5549 Table Lamp, No. A-3325/5543 Table Lamp, No. A-3323/5541 Table Lamp, No. A-3322/5551 Table Lamp and No. A-3368/5550 Floor Lamp.

Fundamentally, of course, the main purpose of a table or floor lamp is to furnish adequate illumination. Thus it is important to make certain that the lamp you select is the proper height, has an appropriate shade and preferably has a three-way socket.

In addition to these very practical requirements, lamps provide one of the most interesting accent pieces in any room. Luckily there is a great variety of lamp styles that blend beautifully with Early American furniture.

First of all, Tell City has styles in warm Andover maple finish. For the homemaker who wants a dash of color, many lamps are offered in a choice of four antiques finishes . . . antique blue, antique green, antique red and antique yellow.

Some decorators prefer to use lamps with ceramic, metal or glass bases to provide an interesting contrast and these styles are available. All in all, yours is a wide choice to utilize these practical lamps for dramatic decorating effects.

In the case of floor lamps, it is important to choose a lamp with a sturdy base—especially if the lamp must support books, spectacles or ash trays.

TELL CITY CHAIR COMPANY
TELL CITY, IND.

TABLE LAMPS

Like the Decorative Accessories, Tell City table lamps pick their theme from Early America. Since candles were the ordinary method of lighting in that period, several designs have bases much like the holders which held tallow candles one hundred years ago.

Other designs found their origin in the tools and everyday articles of the colonists—like the ball-jointed embroidery frame, andiron base and bell ringer lamps.

For variety, Tell City's designer has introduced glass, ceramic and metal decorated bases in a pleasing variety of shapes and sizes.

Each lamp illustrated in the section which follows has a short note giving the history of the design. Besides explaining the design origin, these make interesting conversation for the homemaker who enjoys lamps that are "different."

All lamps have three-way sockets for decorative lighting effects and are U/L approved.

No. 3301/5501 Key Lamp with plain shade (at left). Finely detailed base in shape of giant key. Over-all Height 36". Made of Solid Hard Rock Maple in #48 Andover finish.

No. 3302/5502 Ball-and-Socket Lamp with plain shade (at right). Unusual base is copied from an antique ball-jointed stand originally made to hold an embroidery frame. Over-all Height 35". Made of Solid Hard Rock Maple in #48 Andover finish.

No. 3306/5538 Eagle Lamp
with plain shade (at left).
Solid cast brass eagle on top of massive, round wooden ball. Heavy black base with brass stars. Wonderful in pairs. Over-all Height: 39½". Made of Solid Hard Rock Maple in #48 Andover finish.

**No. 3309/5512
Andiron Lamp**
with plain shade (at right).
Styled from a 17th century andiron. Ideal in pairs. Made of Solid Hard Rock Maple in #48 Andover finish. Over-all Height: 39½".

No. 3311/5514 Table Lamp
with plain shade (at left).
The classic simplicity of design which distinguishes this lamp makes it ideally suited for use in pairs. Over-all Height: 32¼". Made of Solid Hard Rock Maple in #48 Andover finish.

No. 3313/5516 Table Lamp
with plain shade (at right).
A tall lamp with a brass base and a well-proportioned turned column. Ideal for use in pairs. Over-all Height: 40". Made of Solid Hard Rock Maple in #48 Andover finish.

**No. 3317/5516
Candlestick Lamp**
with plain shade (at left).
Adapted from an antique candlestick, this tall lamp features a nice brass base and generous maple turning. Overall Height: 42½″. Made of Solid Hard Rock Maple in #48 Andover finish.

**No. A-3321/5539
Table Lamp**
with plain shade (at right).
Has ceramic base with wooden elements as accents. Overall Height: 31½″. Wooden elements made of Solid Hard Rock Maple in #86 Antique Blue finish, #87 Antique Green finish, #88 Antique Red finish or #89 Antique Yellow finish.

**No. A-3322/5540
Table Lamp**
with plain shade (at left).
The beautiful simplicity of this lamp makes it especially appealing in pairs. Over-all Height: 33″. Made of Solid Hard Rock Maple in #86 Antique Blue finish, #87 Antique Green finish, #88 Antique Red finish or #89 Antique Yellow finish, with brass elements in base.

**No. A-3322/5551
Table Lamp**
with print shade.

**No. 3322/5551
Table Lamp**
with print shade (at right).
Made of Solid Hard Rock Maple in #48 Andover Maple finish.

**No. 3322/5540
Table Lamp**
with plain shade.

No. A-3323/5541 Table Lamp
with plain shade (at left).
This tall living room lamp has a smoked glass base with colored wood accents. Over-all Height: 38¼". Wood accents are made of Solid Hard Rock Maple in #86 Antique Blue finish, #87 Antique Green finish, #88 Antique Red finish or #89 Antique Yellow finish.

No. A-3324/5542 Table Lamp
with plain shade (at right).
A typical Early American lamp in classic design with white milk glass base and wood and brass trim. Over-all Height: 35". Wood trim is made of Solid Hard Rock Maple in #86 Antique Blue finish, #87 Antique Green finish, #88 Antique Red finish or #89 Antique Yellow finish.

No. 3324/5542 Table Lamp same as above except in #48 Andover Maple finish.

No. A-3325/5543 Table Lamp
with plain shade (at left).
This exceptionally tall lamp features a clear glass and brass element on a fluted wood base. Over-all Height: 45". Wood element is made of Solid Hard Rock Maple in #86 Antique Blue finish, #87 Antique Green finish, #88 Antique Red finish or #89 Antique Yellow finish.

No. 3325/5543 Table Lamp same as above except in #48 Andover Maple finish.

No. 3326/5547 Bell Ringer Lamp
with plain shade (at right).
A beautifully proportioned, smaller lamp whose design is based on the bell used by the Town Crier in Early American days. Made of Solid Hard Rock Maple in #48 Andover finish. Bell at bottom is glazed gilt. Over-all Height 26".

No. 3327/5548
Turned Lamp
with plain shade (at left).
A nicely contoured lamp with crisp turnings. Made of Solid Hard Rock Maple in #48 Andover finish with green accents on ball and base. Good for pairs. Over-all Height: 29½".

No. A-3329/5549
Table Lamp
with plain shade (at right).
A strikingly different design that can be used effectively in pairs with a variety of furniture designs. Shade has distinctive trim. Made of Solid Hard Rock Maple and offered in four finishes: #86 Antique Blue finish, #87 Antique Green finish, #88 Antique Red finish and #89 Antique Yellow finish. Over-all Height: 38".

No. 3328/5540
Spindle Lamp
with plain shade (at left).
An unusual base of five turned spindles makes this lamp distinctive and unusual. Made of Solid Hard Rock Maple in #48 Andover finish with green accents. Over-all Height: 33½".

No. 3328/5551
Spindle Lamp
with print shade (at right).
Green accents on the distinctive spindled base make this lamp appealing to Early American enthusiasts. Made of Solid Hard Rock Maple in #48 Andover finish. Over-all Height: 33½".

Distinctive and Practical
FLOOR LAMPS

No. 3360/5534
Cloverleaf Floor Lamp
with plain shade.

The table on this lamp is extra large. Heavy legs give ample support for ash trays, glasses, etc. Over-all Height: 60". Table diameter 18½". Made of Solid Hard Rock Maple in #48 Andover finish.

No. 3361/5535
Ratchet Floor Lamp
with plain shade.

Unusual ratchet device on base allows lamp to be raised or lowered to height desired. Distinctive, unique, quite Early American. Over-all Height: 55" in low position. Can be raised to 72" high. Made of Solid Hard Rock Maple in #48 Andover finish.

No. 3365/5544
Table Floor Lamp
with plain shade.

Heavy wood base and large table. Brass trim on post. Two sockets under shade. Over-all Height: 57". Made of Solid Hard Rock Maple in #48 Andover finish.

These Solid Hard Rock Maple Floor Lamps are practical as well as decorative and unusual. The three-way sockets give you light to read by or work by as well as subdued effects for "mood" lighting. U/L-approved.

**No. 3366/5545
Bridge Floor Lamp**
with plain shade.
The heavy base on this lamp provides ample support for the large table. Brass trim on post. Over-all Height: 56½". Made of Solid Hard Rock Maple in #48 Andover finish.

No. 3368/5550 Floor Lamp
with plain shade.
The many crisp turnings on the sturdy shaft of this basic Early American lamp give it the right touch for Young Republic. Made of Solid Hard Rock Maple in #48 Andover finish. Over-all Height: 57¾".

No. A-3368/5550 Floor Lamp
with plain shade.
Made of Solid Hard Rock Maple in choice of four antique finishes: #86 Antique Blue finish, #87 Antique Green finish. #88 Antique Red finish, #89 Antique Yellow finish. Over-all Height: 57¾".

95

PAUL KRAUSS SUGGESTS:

How to make a FLOOR PLAN

The best way to arrange furniture in a room is to start from scratch with an empty room. Begin with the rug, then install the drapery and, piece by piece, place the right object just where it belongs. This way, you are less apt to make mistakes than by just shifting things around.

In many cases it's not what you do to a room that makes it good so much as what you don't do. The best rooms are the ones that have only the right things. Too often we lose the real bloom by putting just one too many thing in a room, overweighting it. Discarding is one of the toughest tasks everyone faces. It's the same psychological quirk as eating everything on your plate. How much better it would be if the excess went into the garbage can and you stayed five pounds lighter! But from childhood we were taught that there were children starving someplace in the world, so we should not waste food. Now we waste food by abusing our bodies. If you are blessed with an attic or storage area, fill a large box with the things you really don't need in a room. After six months of living without them, ask yourself if you really want them back.

If you are about to move into a new house or can't find the man power to empty the room you intend to redesign, do the entire thing in capsule form with a floor plan. The pocket on the inside back cover of this book contains a planning kit.

It consists of paper ruled off into ¼-inch squares and templates representing various kinds and sizes of furniture. They may be easily cut out of the cardboard as you use them. Draw the sidewalls of your room on the ruled paper, making each square represent one foot. Indicate the doors and windows. Move the cutouts around until you have the effects you want and trace them or paste them in place. This will immediately show you if you have enough leg room between furniture groups, how well you have designed seating arrangements, and whether your room is well balanced. You may also want to mark the pieces for color so you can see how your room balances in these terms. Locate everything, including lamps and tables. And remember, the underfurnished room is much better than the overcrowded one.

Keep all of your figuring in the pocket of this book. You will also find it a handy place for all your clippings and reference material.

How to make a SWATCH CARD

Along with your floor plan, I strongly advise that you make a swatch card. This is simply a piece of white cardboard to which you staple small samples of fabrics, carpet and wall color. All the colors you will be using in the room should be included. You can see at a glance whether or not the colors are harmonious. Don't be misled by the size relationship of the samples to one another. Your wall color sample may be the same 1" x 2" size as a bright piece of fabric. Yet the piece of fabric may represent a very small area like a couch pillow while the wall color will be used in an area one hundred times larger. This makes no difference. It is the color harmony in which you are interested. When talking to painters or in doing the job yourself, be sure you know where one color stops and another begins before you get trapped. This also holds true of where wallpaper stops and paint begins.